EUROPEAN WORKS OF ART

EUROPEAN WORKS OF ART

in the M. H. de Young Memorial Museum

Published by Diablo Press for the de Young Museum Society

© 1966 by the de Young Museum Society and Diablo Press.
Box 7084, Berkeley, California 94717
Made in the United States of America

Library of Congress Catalog Card Number: 66-29482

FOREWORD

The publication of this handbook has been made
possible under the auspices of The de Young
Museum Society, whose publication fund was created
by the late George D. Cameron, president of
the Board of Trustees.

This handbook combines the 1950 Handbook and
the catalogue of the Samuel H. Kress Collection
at the M. H. de Young Memorial Museum,
both long out of print. It is designed to give a concise
exposition of objects in the Museum and to provide
photographic reference for scholars.

The editorial supervision of the handbook
was provided by Edwin F. Carter, Curator-Librarian,
with the assistance of D. Graeme Keith,
Curator of Decorative Arts, and Alden Murray,
Curator of Paintings.

Jack R. McGregor, *Director*
M. H. de Young Memorial Museum

HISTORY OF THE MUSEUM.

At the end of the California Midwinter International Exposition of 1894, the Exposition's Fine Arts Building in Golden Gate Park, together with surplus funds, were turned over to Mr. M. H. de Young, who had served as Director-General of the Exposition, for the purpose of establishing a museum. Some of the Exposition's exhibits were acquired as the nucleus of a collection, and donations by Mr. de Young and other individuals followed. A temporary income to be used for purchases was provided by Mr. de Young who, along with others, also provided funds for the construction of additional buildings.

In 1895, the City of San Francisco undertook the maintenance of the Museum under the jurisdiction of the Park Commission. In 1926 the Museum became a separate department of the City, under its own Board of Trustees. The original name—"Memorial Museum"—was changed to "M. H. de Young Memorial Museum" in 1921 to honor Mr. de Young, then still living, for his great efforts in the development of the Museum.

The cornerstone of the present building was laid in 1917, and the move into these larger quarters was made in 1919. Major additions have been made since, the largest of which is the west wing, which houses the Avery Brundage Collection of Asian Art. It was completed in 1966.

The Museum is one of the most popular in the United States, with an average attendance of more than one million visitors annually over the past decade.

THE COLLECTION.

The great majority of the objects in the Museum have been acquired through the generosity of many individual and group donors. The de Young Museum Society has made many valuable contributions to the permanent collection by means of funds derived from its memberships and special activities such as the sponsorship of loan exhibitions. Certain individuals have established endowment funds to provide for acquisitions on a continuing basis.

It would be impossible in this space to list the names of all those whose public-spirited support has helped bring the Museum to its present status, but wherever their gifts are illustrated in this handbook, due credit has been given.

FRENCH, LIMOGES, 12TH CENTURY.
Crucifix.

Gilt bronze, enameled, and set with stones.
H. 10¾".
Gift of Julius Landauer. 56.03.2.

This Romanesque work is a product of the important center of enamel production at Limoges. The cross is enameled in the *champlevé* technique, in which the depressions intended to receive the enamel colors are produced in the casting. The separately cast figure of the clothed Christ is delicately engraved in many details. Many of these early enamels were decoratively enriched by setting them with semiprecious stones cut as cabochons—the surfaces rounded rather than faceted.

FRENCH, 12TH-13TH CENTURY.
Candlestick.

Gilt bronze and iron.
H. 6⅞″.
Purchased by the City and County of San Francisco.
53.18.1.

This small candlestick of gilded bronze, fitted with
an iron pricket, has tripod supports terminating
in animal feet and a charming punchwork band of
foliated scrolls on the apron below the shaft.

GERMAN, HILDESHEIM, 13TH CENTURY.

Aquamanile (ewer).

Bronze.
H. 9⅝".
Purchased with funds from various donors. 54.22.

During the Romanesque period pouring vessels were frequently made in the form of animals, commonly lions. In this example, the vessel is filled through the covered opening on top of the head and emptied through the spout held in the lion's mouth. The formalized rendering of the facial features and the mane is characteristic of the Romanesque style.

GERMAN, COLOGNE, EARLY 13TH CENTURY.
Corpus from a Crucifix.

Painted wood.
H. 40½".
Gift of Julius Landauer. 56.30.1.

This figure, in the late Romanesque style, gives a sense of the timber from which it was cut. A degree of naturalism begins to show in the folds of the drapery. The representation of the feet separately nailed to the cross is found only in crucifixes earlier than the mid-fourteenth century.

FRENCH, ÎLE DE FRANCE, ABOUT 1250.

Saint Peter.

Walnut.
H. 61½".
Acquired through exchange. 59.17.

Though made of wood, this Gothic figure shows an almost architectural compactness. The growing humanism, characteristic of Gothic painting and sculpture, is to be seen in the naturalistic representation of the drapery and the expressiveness of the forward thrust of the head. The figure is identified by the enormous key.

WEST GERMAN, LATE 13TH CENTURY.

Chest.

Oak and iron.
H. 33¾″, L.80″, W. 27½″.
Gift of Mrs. Betty Walter Sirigo. 59.33.18.

Medieval chests were often roughly made and reinforced with iron straps which, together with the locks, were usually decoratively treated. The straps on this chest are split into three at their ends and wrought into *fleurs-de-lis;* they are secured to the chest by nails with large heads which themselves become a decorative motif. Locks were also ornamentally wrought in a variety of techniques often employing foliate, animal, or architectural motifs. In an age of insecurity, chests conveyed a feeling of strength and portability. Chests also served as beds for servants who laid their crude straw mattresses on top of them.

SPANISH, ABOUT 1300.
Madonna and Child.

Painted and gilded wood.
H. 49½".
Gift of Archer M. Huntington. 45.32.

The strict hieratical frontality of this group from northern Spain, together with the "archaic" smiles of Mary and the Christ Child, are Romanesque characteristics of Byzantine origin. These characteristics de-emphasize the human qualities of the figures and stress their symbolic meaning and sacred nature.

BERNARDO DADDI.

Italian, Florentine, about 1280-1348.

A Crowned Virgin Martyr.

Probably Saint Catherine of Alexandria. Part of a dismantled polyptych. About 1335. Tempera on linden wood panel.
H. 24¼", W. 12".
Gift of the Samuel H. Kress Foundation. 61.44.1.

Saint Catherine, a royal lady of Alexandria, was martyred by Emperor Maximinus II. She is shown holding a palm frond, a symbol of triumph over death, and a book, a symbol of her learning. Daddi, a contemporary and student of Giotto, was influenced by Gothic sculpture and by the Sienese painters Simone Martini and Ambrogio Lorenzetti. This figure shows how, in his later years, Daddi abandoned Giotto's solid forms and reverted to a more archaic, two-dimensional style. In the Opera del Duomo, Florence, there is a full-length figure of Saint Catherine very similar to ours, dated 1334.

MASO DI BANCO.
Italian, Florentine, ?-1346.

Madonna and Child with Saints.

Central panel from a dismantled triptych.
About 1330. Tempera on linden wood panel.
H. 18½″, W. 8½″.
Gift of the Samuel H. Kress Foundation. 61.44.2.

On the left of the Virgin and Child are Saint John
the Baptist, a bishop saint, and Saint Lucy; on
the right are Saint Peter, another bishop saint, and a
martyred saint. In accordance with the medieval
tradition of hieratic scale, the saints, being of
lesser importance than the Madonna and Christ
Child, are smaller. Maso, like Bernardo Daddi,
was a pupil of Giotto, and one of his greatest
followers. He is known for his brilliant colors and
for his *sfumato,* a subtle blending of black and white
underpainting with the color tones
to emphasize the modeling.

19

FRENCH, EARLY 15TH CENTURY.
The Resurrection of Christ *and* Christ Appears
to Saint Mary Magdalen after His
Resurrection.

Two panels from an altarpiece. Oil on wood panel.
H. 40½″, W. 19½″; H. 40⅜″, W. 19½″.
Gift of the Samuel H. Kress Foundation. 61.44.27, 28.

Few French panel paintings of this period have
survived. These pictures may be dated by comparing
them with the illuminated manuscripts of the
period. The framing of the golden background with
an ornamental punched pattern shows the Sienese
influence which reached France during the Avignon
papacy. The plants strewn over the ground are
reminiscent of early fifteenth-century tapestries from
Arras. Some Swiss elements are also present,
particularly the rose hedge in the background and the
profile of Saint Mary. These panels, although
predominantly French in character, are examples of
the international style that swept most of Europe
shortly after the turn of the fifteenth century.

ATTRIBUTED TO
GIOVANNI DEL BIONDO.
Italian, Florentine, 1356-1392.
Madonna and Child Enthroned with Angels.

Tempera on wood panel.
H. 32″, W. 21⅜″.
Gift of Mrs. Herbert Fleishhacker. 46.3.

Although Giovanni is considered to be a follower of Giotto, he frequently turned back to an earlier tradition. The rigid frontality of the Madonna and the vapid, frozen expressions of the figures are more reminiscent of the style of the thirteenth century than of Giotto's work. Here Giovanni uses the traditional gold background of Byzantine and early Italian painting. He was, however, capable of executing paintings in the "modern" manner with naturalistic figures and spacial definition.

21

FRENCH, METZ, ABOUT 1350.
Madonna and Child.

Limestone.
H. 50½″.
Purchased by the City and County of San Francisco.
55360.

In this Gothic work the Madonna and Child are not
only religious symbols, they are also a human
mother and child. This impression is created by a
realistic portrayal. Also, the gentle "S" movement of
the standing figure, the quiet lines of the drapery,
and the gestures and facial expressions emphasize the
human relationships. Medieval statues were
originally painted in naturalistic colors. Small traces
of paint are still to be seen in this group.

ANTONIO VENEZIANO.
Italian, Tuscan, about 1313-1387.
Saint Paul.

Wing from a dismantled polyptych.
About 1385. Tempera on poplar panel.
H. 42¼″, W. 17⅜″.
Gift of the Samuel H. Kress Foundation. 61.44.4.

Saint Paul, the first great missionary of the Christian
church, holds the sword of his martyrdom and a
book of his Epistles. Evidently of Venetian origin,
Antonio worked in Pisa, Siena, and
Florence; his works are very rare. This massive,
statuesque figure, with voluminous drapery folds and
deeply modeled features, is typical of his style.
Antonio represents a high point of
fourteenth-century panel painting in Florence.

LUCA DI TOMMÈ.
Italian, Sienese, about 1330-1389.
Crucifixion.

About 1370. Tempera on linden wood panel.
H. 16⅛″, W. 23½″.
Gift of the Samuel H. Kress Foundation. 61.44.3.

In 1355 Luca di Tommè di Nuto became a member of the painters' guild. He is mentioned repeatedly in the city records of Siena, both as an artist and as a member of the city government. He was active also in Orvieto. Luca's painting style was influenced by the older Sienese artists Simone Martini, Lippo Memmi and Pietro Lorenzetti. This picture, originally the center panel of the predella of an altarpiece, is of the same period as Luca's *Christ Crucified Between His Mother and St. John,* signed and dated 1366, now in the museum at Pisa. Some details are similar, but there is more rhythm in the composition of our *Crucifixion.* It carries forward the great tradition of Sienese painting of the first half of the fourteenth century.

SOUTH EUROPEAN, LATE 14TH CENTURY.

The Lord Reprimanding Adam and Eve.

Alabaster.
H. 20¼″, W. 25⅝″.
Gift of The de Young Museum Society. 59.40.

This work shows a scene before the expulsion from the Garden of Eden as related in the Book of Genesis. The barely visible textile pattern in Jehovah's robe is well known in late fourteenth- and fifteenth- century brocaded velvets. Originally the pattern was probably painted on the stone. Note the distortion in scale between the figures and the trees in the background.

FRENCH, ABOUT 1350.
Crucifixion.

Ivory.
H. 3⅜″.
Gift of the M. H. de Young Endowment Fund. 59.8.

This relief was probably one-half of a folding portable diptych used for private devotions, the missing half of which almost certainly represented the Virgin and Child. The crucifixion is framed in a Gothic architectural setting. The finely sculptured scene is charged with emotion despite its small size. The representation of Mary's sorrow by her being pierced by the lance that wounded Christ is based on the description of the Presentation in the Temple in Saint John's Gospel in which Simeon says to Mary: "Yea, a sword shall pierce through thy soul also."

FRENCH, BURGUNDIAN, LATE 14TH CENTURY.

Head of a Saint.

Limestone.
H. 9¾″.
Gift of the M. H. de Young Endowment Fund.
54578.

This sculptured head retains much of its charm despite the loss of its nose. The formal aspects of the sculpture are of a high order and remain virtually undisturbed by what, in a lesser work, would have been a serious loss. A comparison of the textures of the face and of the shawl and wavy hair reveals the various types of chisels used in the carving. The head is a fragment from a larger work.

FRENCH, 1350-1400.

Madonna and Child.

Limestone.
H. 29".
Gift of Mr. and Mrs. George T. Cameron. 44.22.

When one compares this seated group with the formalized, hieratical representation found in the Spanish Romanesque Madonna and Child (page 17), one sees how Gothic naturalism has infused the subject with human feeling. The Christ child holds the dove and the scepter, symbols of his divinity and dominion.

FRENCH,
SECOND HALF OF 14TH CENTURY.
Madonna and Child.

Boxwood (partly painted and gilded) and silver.
H. 9″.
Gift of the M. H. de Young Endowment Fund.
54676.

Boxwood is a hard, close-grained wood which was often used for small sculptures. The Madonna is clothed in fourteenth-century dress and wears a silver crown. The pose of the seated figure and the quiet rhythm of the deeply cut folds of the dress give the figure a queenly dignity.

FRENCH, EARLY 15TH CENTURY.
Reliquary.

Gilt silver.
H. 14".
Purchased by the City and County of San Francisco
47.3.1.

The relic which this reliquary originally held was
displayed in the cylindrical vessel beneath the
figure of the angel. Reliquaries were sometimes made
in the form of that part of the body from which
the relic came. In other instances the relic was given
an architectural setting, in this case in the Gothic
style. The knobbed stem and lobed feet, similar to
those used on chalices, provide support for the
reliquary and facilitate its display during religious
processions.

ITALIAN, 15TH CENTURY.
Reliquary.

Gilt copper.
H. 17½″.
Gift of the M. H. de Young Endowment Fund.
53.18.3.

As the form of this reliquary indicates,
it was made to display a bone from
the forearm of a saint. Such reliquaries were often
made of silver, but they were also fashioned from less
costly metals, such as copper, and then gilded.

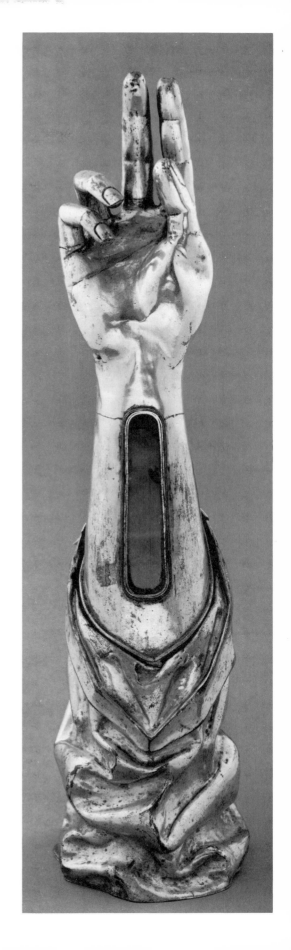

WEST GERMAN OR FRENCH,
ABOUT 1390.
Saint Christopher.

Linden wood.
H. 30¾".
Gift of Mr. and Mrs. Ralph C. Lee. 59.32.

Saint Christopher was a legendary giant who
had been converted to Christianity and, as a work
of charity, devoted himself to carrying wayfarers
across a bridgeless river. When the Christ child
asked to be ferried across, Saint Christopher carried
him on his shoulder; his burden, as he made his way
across the river, grew so heavy that it seemed to him
that he carried the weight of the world. When he
complained of this the Christ child replied: "Marvel
not, for thou hast borne on thy back the world
and Him who created it."

FLEMISH, DINAND, ABOUT 1425.
Jug.

Bronze.
H. 9½″.
Gift of Messrs. E. and A. Silberman. 44.25.

A typical late medieval jug of boldly modeled silhouette. The repetition with variation of the stepped moldings at the foot, base of the neck, and the cover adds greatly to the interest of the form. The "animal style" of early Christian and medieval art of northern Europe survives in the handle and spout forms. Dinand was such an important center for the manufacture of bronze vessels and utensils that the town's name became the generic term for this whole class of objects which is known today as "dinanderie."

BICCI DI LORENZO.
Italian, Florentine, 1373-1452.
Saint Anthony and Saint Stephen *and*
Saint John the Baptist and Saint Miniato.

Tempera on poplar panel.
H. 61¾″, W. 21⅛″; H. 60½″, W. 21½″.
Gift of the M. H. de Young Endowment Fund.
54869 A-B.

These two wings from an altarpiece portray Saint
Anthony, the first monastic (with a hog
at his feet symbolizing gluttony, indicating
his triumph over sin) with Saint Stephen, the
first Christian martyr (with stones, by which he was
martyred), and Saint John the Baptist (with his
hair shirt and reed cross) with Saint Miniato
of Florence (crowned, holding a palm frond and a
javelin).
Bicci was influenced by the courtly painter Gentile
da Fabriano. He had a large studio and catered
to the taste of the Florentine upper class, using the
graceful, aristocratic Gothic figure style popular
in Florence in the 1430's.

TADDEO DI BARTOLO.
Italian, Sienese, 1362-1422.
Crowned Madonna Nursing Her Child.

Central panel of a dismantled polyptych. About 1400.
Tempera on poplar panel.
H. 40¾", W. 24½".
Gift of the Samuel H. Kress Foundation. 61.44.6.

This painting is comparable to one dated 1403 in the museum in Perugia. Taddeo was the last important Sienese master of the fourteenth century. Although he worked chiefly in Siena, he also painted in several other Italian cities, especially Genoa, Pisa, San Gimignano and Perugia. He has the characteristic Sienese feeling for decoration and color, as seen in the elaborate fabrics, and for elegant line, as seen in the Madonna's veil and hands. Many critics agree that this is probably the finest of Taddeo's Madonna paintings.

GIOVANNI DI MARCO DAL PONTE.
Italian, Florentine, 1385-about 1437.
Madonna and Child with Four Angels.

About 1430. Tempera on fruitwood panel.
H. 46¾″, W. 26¾″.
Gift of the Samuel H. Kress Foundation. 61.44.5.

This picture, painted late in Giovanni's career, shows the transitional stage in Florentine painting—from the medieval stylization of the fourteenth century to the greater realism of the generation of Masaccio in the fifteenth. The figures embody the latest knowledge of three-dimensional drawing, yet they have traditional flat halos, not drawn in perspective. The graceful, linear charm of the figures and their gestures is reminiscent of Giovanni's contemporary, Lorenzo Monaco.

FRA GIOVANNI ANGELICO.
Italian, Florentine, 1387-1455.
The Meeting of Saint Francis and Saint Dominic.

Tempera on poplar panel.
H. 10½″, W. 10⅛″.
Gift of the Samuel H. Kress Foundation. 61.44.7.

This panel commemorates the meeting of the founders of two Christian orders, the Franciscans and the Dominicans. Fra Angelico was influenced by Masaccio, using his deep space. However, his tender, refined figures are reminiscent of the Sienese gracefulness of line of the previous century, which influenced many Florentines not following Giotto, such as Lorenzo Monaco, Fra Angelico's master. This panel and four others illustrating the life of Saint Francis, now in Berlin, Altenburg, and the Vatican, probably formed the *predella* of the altarpiece in the San Marco Museum, Florence, which Fra Angelico painted for the Franciscan monastery Bosco ai Frati.

BARTOLOMEO DEGLI ERRI.

Italian, Modenese, active 1460-1476.

The Debate with the Heretic and Christ Approving Saint Thomas' Work *and* The Vision of Fra Paolino dell'Aquila.

Two panels from an altarpiece.
Tempera on fruitwood panel.
H. 17⅝″, W. 13⅛″; H. 17¾″, W. 13⅜″.
Gift of the Samuel H. Kress Foundation.
61.44.10, 11.

These two panels are part of an altarpiece illustrating the life of Saint Thomas Aquinas. The first portrays Thomas debating with a heretic (who wears a turban); Thomas appears again in the background, receiving Christ's approval of his work. The second portrays a vision that occurred to Fra Paolino dell'Aquila, the Inquisitor of Naples, shortly after the death of Saint Thomas. He saw the dead saint seated upon the bishop's throne whereupon Saint Paul entered and, after speaking briefly, ushered Thomas from the consistory (at the left of the panel).

THE MASTER OF THE LANCKORONSKI ANNUNCIATION.

Italian, Florentine, about 1445.

The Annunciation.

Tempera on wood panel.
H. 10″, W. 13⅛″.
Gift of The de Young Museum Society. 54.3.

The Archangel Gabriel tells the Virgin Mary that she will bear the Christ child. The presence of God is indicated by the rays on which hovers the dove of the Holy Ghost; the lilies in the foreground are a symbol of the purity of the Virgin.

This painting was formerly in the collection of Count Lanckoronski of Vienna, whose name is used to indicate an unknown painter related in style to both Fra Angelico and Domenico Veneziano. It has been suggested that this painting could be an early work by Francesco Pesellino, who was active in this period. The artist is as concerned with the architectural setting as with the delicate, graceful, figures.

BARTOLOMEO DI GIOVANNI.
Italian, Florentine, ?-1511.
The Adoration of the Magi.

About 1490. Tempera and oil on poplar panel.
Diam. 37½″.
Gift of the Samuel H. Kress Foundation. 61.44.13.

This painting is typical of the High Renaissance, with its classical elements of architecture and deep, clearly ordered perspective. It is extremely close in style to Bartolomeo's only documented work, a *predella* painted in 1488 for Domenico Ghirlandaio's altarpiece in the Hospital of the Innocents in Florence. He was evidently familiar with Leonardo da Vinci's unfinished *Adoration,* as some of the horses and figures were clearly inspired by that work. Other elements in the painting derive from Ghirlandaio and, to a certain extent, from Botticelli.

41

MATTEO DI GIOVANNI.
Italian, Sienese, about 1430-1495.
The Magi before Herod *and* The Crucifixion.

Two panels from an altarpiece. About 1491.
Tempera on poplar panel.
H. 11¾", W. 27"; H. 11¾", W. 26¾".
Gift of the Samuel H. Kress Foundation. 61.44.8, 9.

Matteo was born in the Umbrian town of Borgo San
Sepulcro, where he became familiar with the
works of the Florentine master Piero della Francesca.
A pupil of Vecchietta, Matteo had moved to Siena
by 1450, when the influence of Pollaiuolo becomes
evident. He successfully assimilated the accurate
perspective of the Florentine masters into his
work, and thus became one of the most prominent
and productive Sienese painters of the fifteenth
century. These panels are probably from the
predella of Matteo's altarpiece *The Massacre of the
Innocents* painted in 1491 for the church of
Santa Maria dei Servi in Siena.

FRANCO-RHENISH, ABOUT 1450.

Bishop Saint.

Limestone with traces of polychrome.
H. 43½".
Gift of the M. H. de Young Endowment Fund.
54576.

This unidentified bishop is portrayed in full ceremonial attire. He wears a "Gothic" chasuble and mitre and carries a crozier in his left hand. The embroidered decoration of the chasuble and mitre is executed in considerable detail.

FRENCH, SECOND HALF OF 15TH CENTURY.

The Holy Trinity (Mercy-Seat).

Limestone.
H. 60½″.
Gift of The de Young Museum Society. 53.11.

The doctrine of the Trinity, formulated by St. Augustine (A.D. 354-430), was seldom represented in the visual arts until the fourteenth century when a revival of Augustinianism occurred. God the Father is shown as a seated, bearded patriarch clothed in ecclesiastical garments and wearing a papal tiara. The figure of Christ, on a smaller scale, is shown crucified on the cross held by God. The Holy Spirit as a dove perches with outstretched wings on top of the cross.

ATTRIBUTED TO FRIEDRICH PACHER.
Austrian, Tyrolese, about 1435-1508.
Saint Catherine.

Oil on wood panel. H. 18¼″, W. 17½″.
Gift of Mrs. Herbert Fleishhacker. 51.40.

Saint Catherine holds the wheel on which she was tortured and the sword with which she was beheaded. The instrument of torture should be a spiked wheel, but this rural Tyrolese painter shows instead a simple cart wheel. Friedrich was the brother of Michael Pacher, the outstanding figure in late Gothic painting in the Tyrol. The two collaborated on the high altar at Sankt Wolfgang in Salzkammergut, a carved and painted altarpiece more than thirty feet high. The delicate treatment of the features and the tracery of the crown show the persistence of Gothic mannerism in northern Europe long after it had been supplanted in Italy.

GERMAN, RHENISH,
EARLY 15TH CENTURY.

Saint Mary Magdalen.

Oil on wood panel.
H. 9¾", W. 7¾".
Purchased by the City and County of San Francisco.
48.5.

Mary Magdalen holds the jar of ointment with which she anointed the feet of Christ at the time of her conversion, and then again after his crucifixion. In the other hand she holds a book, referring to her journey to Marseilles, spreading the gospels.
This small panel with its graceful figure reveals a strong influence of miniature painting.

SOUTH GERMAN, PROBABLY SWABIAN, ABOUT 1450.

The Death of the Virgin.

Oil on wood panel.
H. 36⅛″, W. 24⅛″.
Gift of Bertram Newhouse. 44.19.

The dying Virgin is surrounded by the twelve apostles, with Saint Peter at the head of the deathbed and Saint John at the foot. By mid-century the influence of Flemish painting had pervaded all of Germany; in this picture, the facial types and the tubular drapery folds are close to the style of Rogier van der Weyden. The use of flat gold halos at this late date is an archaic feature. The apostles are calm yet their eyes reflect a stunned anguish, emphasized by the crowding of the figures in the small room. This emotionalism is a dominant characteristic throughout much German art of all periods.

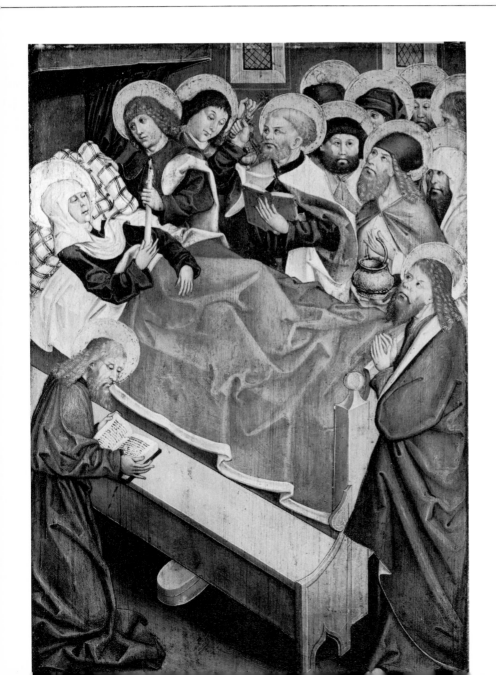

AUSTRIAN, PROBABLY TYROLESE, LATE 15TH CENTURY.

The Last Judgment.

Tempera and oil on pine panel.
H. 57⅝", W. 34⅜".
Gift of the Samuel H. Kress Foundation. 61.44.32.

As angels with trumpets call the dead to judgment, Christ blesses the elect with his right hand and relegates the damned to hell with his left. At the top two angels carry symbols of his Passion: column and scourge, the crown of thorns, the cross and nails. Below, the Virgin and Saint John the Baptist pray to Christ for mercy on mankind. At the left one of the elect gives thanks to him, while on the right a damned soul is being carried away by the devil.

This panel is the central section of a polyptych, the other four panels of which are in the Ruzicka Foundation in Zürich. The painter is most likely Tyrolese, since in addition to the marked Germanic-Flemish influences he shows a knowledge of the regional painting of northern Austria.

THE MASTER OF KAPPENBERG.
German, Westphalian, early 16th century.

The Flagellation *and*
The Crowning with Thorns.

Oil on wood panel.
H. 29¼", W. 41¼".
Purchased by the City and County of San Francisco.
51.4.1.

Two successive scenes from the passion of Christ are shown on one panel, divided by the column in the center. The figure bearing a royal sceptre, standing behind the column uniting the two scenes, may be Herod who, according to the gospel of Saint Luke, was present at the scourging of Christ. This unidentified Westphalian painter was trained in the atelier of the Dünwegge brothers. Although still working in the medieval tradition, he shows a thorough knowledge of correct perspective. The eccentric costumes, with their puffed and slashed sleeves, were commonly worn by the mercenary soldiers of the Emperor Maximilian. The graphic portrayal of Christ's wounds is typical of the medieval German expressionism that reached its height in the paintings of Grünewald.

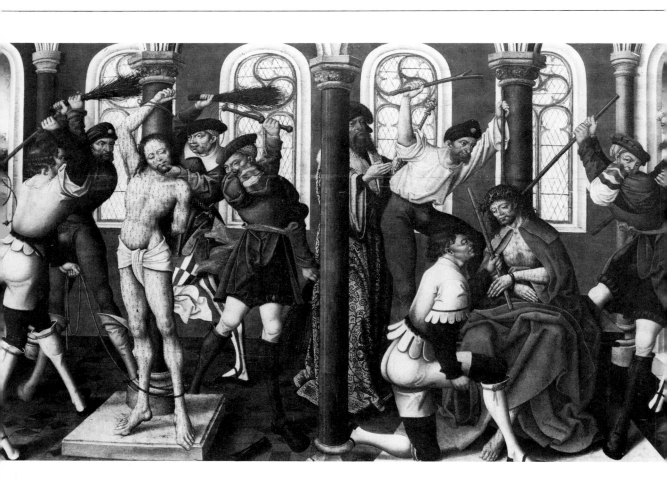

FRANCO-FLEMISH, ABOUT 1500.
Christ Seated on Calvary.

Oak with traces of polychrome.
H. 52¼".
Gift of M. H. de Young. 6545.

The subject of Christ awaiting his death on Calvary
first appears in European art about 1400. This
figure is not the Ecce Homo, as the skull of Adam
at Christ's feet identifies the location as Golgotha, or
Calvary; nor is it the post-crucifixion figure of the
Merciful Christ, as he does not display the wounds of
the crucifixion.

SOUTH GERMAN, BAVARIAN, LATE 15TH CENTURY.

Burial of the Virgin.

Painted wood.
H. 20¼″, L. 34½″.
Gift of Mr. and Mrs. Ralph C. Lee. 48.9.

The draped coffin is being carried by the Apostles. According to legend the fallen figure in the middle is the High Priest, who dropped dead upon touching the coffin. The Old Testament parallel is the prohibition upon pain of death against touching the Ark of the Covenant. The various facial types are executed with great individuality.

SOUTH GERMAN, ABOUT 1480.
Martyrdom of Saint Lawrence.

Linden wood.
H. 15½", L. 27⅞".
Gift of Mrs. Betty Walter Sirigo. 57.18.3.

St. Lawrence was archdeacon to Sixtus II, bishop of Rome, into whose care, according to the legend, the bishop placed the treasures of the Church. Before his own martyrdom in A.D.258 Sixtus commanded his archdeacon to distribute the possessions of the Church to the poor. When the prefect of Rome demanded that St. Lawrence surrender the treasures, he presented to him a great crowd of the poor and sick, saying that these were the treasures of the Church of Christ. The infuriated prefect had him executed by fire in the manner shown.

GERMAN, RHENISH, EARLY 16TH CENTURY.
Saint Boniface.

Linden wood.
H. 71".
Purchased with funds from various donors. 46.8.1.

St. Boniface was an English monk who became bishop of Mainz and spent his life evangelizing the Germans; he died in a massacre near Dockum in A.D. 745. The nearly life-size figure is holding a book in his left hand symbolizing his teaching mission. In his right hand he probably originally held a palm, symbolic of his martyrdom. The great flourish of drapery in the lower part of the figure is characteristic of much German sculpture in this period, which had a tendency toward the flamboyant.

GERMAN, RHENISH, ABOUT 1480.
Saint James the Less (?).

Linden wood.
H. 66½″.
Purchased with funds from various donors. 46.8.2.

St. James the Less was one of the Apostles. He was
martyred by being beaten to death with a club.
As the instrument of his martyrdom is missing the
identification of the subject is uncertain. This work is
probably by the same hand which carved the
St. Boniface opposite.

ITALIAN, DERUTA, ABOUT 1525.
Plate.

Tin-glazed earthenware.
Diam. 16½″.
Gift of Jakob Goldschmidt. 53.40.4.

Deruta was an important center for the manufacture of Italian majolica or faience (tin-glazed earthenware). The artists of Deruta made a specialty of decorating their wares with lustre colors in shades varying from copper to gold. The lustre techniques reached Italy through Islamic Spain probably by way of the potters of Valencia, a center famous for its lustre wares. These wares were exported to Italy via the island of Majorca, which name, in the corrupted form of "Majolica," has since become the generic term for all tin-glazed earthenwares. The subject represented is not known, but the figure losing his horns probably is a satyr or a cuckold.

SPANISH, ABOUT 1460.
Albarello (drug jar).

Glazed earthenware.
H. 12¼".
Gift of The de Young Museum Society. 53.36.1.

This drug jar is an early example of tin-glazed
earthenware with lustre decoration. It is in
the so-called "Hispano-Moresque" style which
combines Spanish and Moorish elements of design.
The over-all foliate decoration in gold lustre
and blue is typical of many of these fifteenth-century
jars. The technique of lustre decoration came
to Europe through Spain from the Islamic potters
of the Near East when Spain was a part of the
Islamic world.

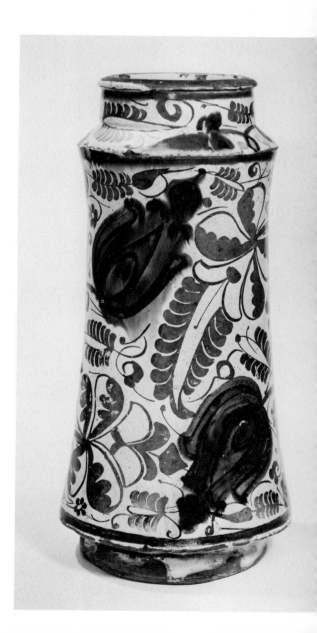

ANDREA DEL VERROCCHIO.
Italian, Florentine, 1435–1488.

Reclining Putto.

About 1480–1488. Marble. H. 11¼″, L. 20½″.
Gift of The de Young Museum Society. 49.5.

This work is based on a sketch by Verrocchio
in the Louvre. The modeling of the figure
has been compared to other works by him
such as the *Putto with a Dolphin*
in Florence. It is thought that this work may be
connected with the unfinished fountain commissioned
in 1488 by Matthias Corvinus, King of Hungary.

BARTOLOMMEO VIVARINI.
Italian, Venetian, active about 1450-1500.
Madonna and Child.

Signed and dated: "Bartholomeus Vivarinus
de Muriano Pinxit 1481."
Tempera and oil on wood panel.
H. 23¼", W. 17½".
Gift of the M. H. de Young Endowment Fund.
54459.

Vivarini worked with his brother Antonio;
they were influenced by Gentile da Fabriano
and the leading Venetian painters
Mantegna and Giovanni Bellini.

In this picture, with its exceptional clarity
of outline and boldness of modelling, the artist
portrays the infant Christ asleep on a parapet
in the foreground, an archaic theme derived from
Byzantine tradition.

GENTILE BELLINI.
Italian, Venetian, 1429-1507.

The Doge Leonardo Loredano.

About 1501. Oil on parchment stretched on wood panel. H. 13", W. 10¼".
Gift of The de Young Museum Society. 50.11.

The *Doge* (duke) of Venice was elected for life by a body of eleven electors from among the aristocracy. Since it was customary to have an official portrait painted of each new office-holder, a large but effective group of these paintings exists. Here, Loredano is shown wearing the *corno,* the traditional horned cap of office. His features are modeled with thin, crisp lines, lit entirely from the right. It is a highly formal portrait in profile, in the tradition of classical imperial coin and medal portraiture revived by Gentile's predecessor Pisanello. It is thought to be a sketch from life, retained in the artist's studio to form the basis of larger, official versions, none of which have survived.

BARTOLOMMEO MONTAGNA.
Italian, Venetian, about 1450-1523.
Saint Bernard and a Holy Bishop.

Tempera and oil on wood panel.
H. 25″, W. 27″.
Purchased by the City and County of San Francisco.
50.7.

San Bernardino, the great spiritual leader of the twelfth century, is shown in a Cistercian habit, holding a book of his writings. The bishop is not identified. Montagna lived and worked in Vicenza, a provincial center dominated by the Venetian school. His figures have weight and power; the portrait of the bishop is especially compelling. In common with many Venetians, he used brilliant, enamel-like colors.

RAFFAELLINO DEL GARBO, or DE KROLIS.

Italian, Florentine, about 1470–1524.

Madonna Enthroned with Saint Jerome and Saint Bartholomew.

Signed "RAPHAEL DE KROLIS Pinxit A. D. MCCCCCII." Oil on poplar panel. H. 78", W. 84½".
Gift of the Samuel H. Kress Foundation. 61.44.12.

On the left is Saint Jerome, with the lion he tamed, on the right is Saint Bartholomew, holding the knife with which he was flayed alive. Raffaellino's work was highly popular in his native Florence. He apparently was familiar with the graceful works of the Perugine painter Pinturicchio, yet he retained the solid figures common to almost all Florentine masters. This altarpiece was painted for the chapel of the Corsini family in the church of S. Spirito, Florence.

CESARE DA SESTO.
Italian, Lombard, about 1477-1523.

The Madonna between Saint John the Baptist
and Saint George.

About 1514. Oil on wood panel. H. 100¼", W. 81".
Gift of the Samuel H. Kress Foundation. 61.44.15.

Cesare was active in Milan, Rome, and Messina.
Saint John the Baptist, carrying a reed cross,
and Saint George, clad in armor, are the patron
saints of Genoa. The fact that these two saints are
shown confirms, in addition to documentation, the
identification of this picture as the one that
Cesare painted in about 1514 for San Domenico, the
church of the Genoese in Messina. When the artist
was in Milan he was influenced by Leonardo
da Vinci, and later in Rome by Raphael. Some of
the reliefs on the Virgin's throne are clearly inspired
by Raphael's frescoes in the Stanza della
Segnatura in the Vatican.

BONIFAZIO VERONESE.

Italian, Venetian, 1487–1533.

The Holy Family with Saint Mary Magdalen, Saint Francis, and the Donor.

Oil on canvas. H 60″, W. 80½″.
Gift of the M. H. de Young Endowment Fund. 48.4.

Bonifazio was a pupil of Palma Vecchio, a painter of Giorgione's generation. Probably the head of the donor seen in the background, worshiping the Holy Family, was painted by Palma. The background of this painting shows the rising interest of Venetian painters in landscape that developed as Venetians became accustomed to owning country villas on the mainland.

ITALIAN, VENETIAN, EARLY 16TH CENTURY.

Portrait of a Young Man Holding a Book.

Oil on canvas.
H. 27⅛″, W. 22½″.
Gift of the Samuel H. Kress Foundation. 61.44.16.

This sensitive painting portrays a pensive young man reading, perhaps some poetry. He wears a glove which leaves one fingertip bare, perhaps to facilitate turning the pages, a feature found in other Italian portraits of the period. The identity of the painter is in question; the work has been variously attributed to Giorgione, Licinio, Pordenone and, most recently, to Giovanni Cariani.

**ITALIAN, PADUAN,
EARLY 16TH CENTURY.**
Candelabrum.

Bronze.
H. 64¾".
Gift of the Samuel H. Kress Foundation. 61.35.

Such monumental candelabra in a figural style gave the Renaissance sculptor great scope for the exercise of his skill in representing the nude. As the Renaissance man sought to revive the civilization of ancient Rome in literature, architecture, sculpture, painting, and the decorative arts, it was inevitable that the human figure would be exploited visually as it was in classical times. The style of the candelabrum connects it with the workshop of Andrea Riccio.

BENVENUTO CELLINI.

Italian, Florentine, 1500–1571.

Cosimo I de' Medici, Grand Duke of Tuscany.

Greek marble.
H. 38", W. 26".
Lent by the Roscoe and Margaret Oakes Foundation.
L 52.10.

This magnificent portrait bust of Cosimo I de' Medici, Grand Duke of Tuscany, is a replica of a much larger bronze which Cellini executed for the Duke in 1547. Contemporary records indicate that the Duke also commissioned from Cellini a bust of himself in Greek marble, a work which in the intervening centuries had become lost. This bust, which is of Greek marble and displays a number of details characteristic of Cellini's hand, is thought by art historians to be the lost portrait by Cellini.

JACOPO CARUCCI DA PONTORMO.
Italian, Florentine, 1494-1557.
Madonna and Child with Two Angels.

About 1523. Oil on linden wood panel.
H. 40¼″, W. 31″.
Gift of the Samuel H. Kress Foundation. 61.44.14.

Pontormo was one of the creators of the anti-classical style called "Mannerism." After the problems of naturalistic representation had been solved anew during the Renaissance, artists turned to the intentional distortion of figures for emotional effect, rejecting the rigid, "universal" laws of proportion. Pontormo himself was a shy, introspective man, and he expressed this mood in this slender Madonna, with her neck, arms, and hands gracefully elongated, her glance turned wistfully downward. A somewhat smaller variant of this panel is in the Palazzo Corsini, Florence.

AGNOLO BRONZINO (AGNOLO DI COSIMO DE MARIANO).

Italian, Florentine, 1503-1572.

Portrait of an Elderly Lady.

Oil on poplar panel.
H. 50″, W. 39⅜″.
Gift of the Samuel H. Kress Foundation. 53670.

Bronzino, the leading Florentine portrait painter of the mid-sixteenth century, had a meticulous technique which imparts to his portraits every convincing aspect except warmth. He was ideally suited to record the features of his patron Cosimo I and his court. The identity of this formidable old lady has never been established. It was thought that she might be Michelangelo's correspondent Vittoria Colonna of Rome, and more recently the name of Maria Salviati of Florence has been suggested. A pupil of Raffaellino del Garbo and of Pontormo, Bronzino was also subject to the pervasive influence of Michelangelo. He was also the author of religious and allegorical compositions in the most advanced Mannerist style.

TITIAN (TIZIANO VECELLIO).
Italian, Venetian, about 1490-1576.

Portrait of a Friend of Titian.

About 1540. Oil on canvas.
H. 35½″, W. 28½″.
Gift of the Samuel H. Kress Foundation. 61.44.17.

The sitter for this penetrating study holds a piece of paper with the inscription DI TITIANO VECELLIO SINGOLARE AMICO, identifying him only as a good friend of the artist. This portrait, with the beautifully lighted, finely drawn face and hands contrasting with the somber darkness of the clothing and the background, was executed during Titian's mature period, shortly after 1540.

TINTORETTO (JACOPO ROBUSTI).
Italian, Venetian, 1518–1594.
Young Man of the Renialme Family.

Oil on canvas.
H. 39½", W. 29¾".
Gift of Dr. and Mrs. Rudolf J. Heinemann. 52.26.

The fertile imagination of Tintoretto provided the most strikingly original interpretations of Biblical and classical themes to be found in Venetian Renaissance painting. His decorations for the Scuola di San Rocco, the Ducal Palace, and numerous churches give ample testimony to his extraordinary genius. All this has tended to overshadow his gifts in the more modest field of portraiture. Here he describes the figure with soft, sketchy brushwork concentrating all the detail in the face, and emphasizes the quiet mood with a dim light.

AUSTRIAN, 15TH CENTURY.
A King or One of the Magi.
Painted and gilded wood.
H. 51".
Gift of Mr. and Mrs. Ralph C. Lee. 48.10.

This slender, armor-clad figure with its refined features has much of the courtly elegance of the late Gothic period. The sweeping curve of the graceful stance contrasts with the lesser rhythms of the lines of the enveloping cloak and the cascade of curling hair. The objects once held by this regal personage have not survived.

FRANCO-FLEMISH, TOURNAI, ABOUT 1475.

Rabbit-Hunting with Ferrets.

Tapestry, silk and wool.
H. 10', W. 12'.
Gift of the M. H. de Young Endowment Fund.
39.4.1.

Tapestries played an important role in the medieval interior, serving as decoration and, to a certain extent, as a means of keeping out the cold. This rare, early tapestry in the *mille fleurs* style is unusual in that it represents a genre subject rather than the courtly, religious or mythological subjects more commonly found. Against a flat background of plant and animal forms, interrupted only by peasant figures in contemporary dress, one sees the lively activity of the hunt. The hunters are using ferrets to chase the rabbits from their burrows into the nets held by other hunters.

FLEMISH, BRUSSELS, ABOUT 1525.
Tapestry.

Wool and silk.
H. 14', W. 26'8".
Gift of the William Randolph Hearst Foundation.
54.14.1.

This is the first of a cycle of nine tapestries on the subject of the Redemption of Man of which this museum possesses four. In this tapestry the Trinity is represented seven times—once enthroned, and six times for the six days of Creation. At the right is represented the Temptation and Fall of Man and the resulting expulsion of Adam and Eve from the Garden of Eden. One sees the survival of the *mille fleurs* style in the lower part of the tapestry. The narrow foliate border is characteristic of tapestries of the late medieval period.

SOUTHERN FRENCH OR FLEMISH, ABOUT 1505.

Christ Carrying the Cross.

Oil on wood panel.
H. 18½″, W. 19½″.
Gift of Mr. and Mrs. George T. Cameron. 47.8.

There is virtually no precedent for the unique trefoil shape of this fascinating panel, and no satisfactory solution has been offered as to what use or purpose may have dictated it. The medieval tradition of portraying consecutive events in one scene is followed. In the foreground Christ struggles with the cross, aided by Simon of Cyrene, while in the background the crucifixion has already taken place.

The authorship of this beautiful picture has been the subject of much speculation. The most recent study suggests that in iconography it is related to a tryptich in St. Antoine, Loches, by a master of the school of Jean Fouquet, but that in style it is more closely related to Flemish painting.

FRENCH, PROVENÇAL, ABOUT 1500.
The Adoration of the Shepherds.

Oil on walnut panel.
H. 11½″, W. 18⅞″.
Gift of the Samuel H. Kress Foundation. 61.44.29.

This Adoration is unusual in that it portrays
the Virgin absorbed in reading a book, presumably
a reference to the Old Testament prophecies of
the Messiah.

This painting belongs to a group
of panels in various collections believed to be
the work of Nicolas Dipre, a native of Amiens who
settled in Avignon in 1495. Originally the panels may
all have formed one altarpiece, although their
variation in size indicates that they did not belong
together. Southern French painting was influenced
by Flanders and near-by Piedmont, but this
artist, with his extremely short, stocky figures, has a
highly individualistic style.

GERMAN, ABOUT 1500.
Pendant.

Gilt silver.
H. 8".
Gift of Julius Landauer. 60.2.6.

This pendant has some connection with the Guild of St. Sebastian (crossbowmen), as is evident from the inclusion of the figures of Christ crucified on a crossbow and St. Sebastian. The Virgin and Child occupy the center of the pendant. The combination of foliate and figural elements in jewelry was characteristic of the medieval and Renaissance periods when craftsmanship played a more important role than the display of costly gems. Typical of the late Gothic style is the rich foliate enframement with its curled leaves.

GERMAN, ABOUT 1500.
Coffer.

Iron.
H. 7", L. 10", W. 6½".
Gift of the California Midwinter Fair Commission.
4998.

This small Gothic wrought-iron coffer is built like a strong box. The three bands with the pierced ornamentation were made with saws, chisels, and files.

MASTER OF THE *RETABLE OF THE REYES CATÓLICOS.*

Spanish, Valladolid, late 15th century.

The Annunciation *and*
The Adoration of the Christ Child.

Two panels from a retable. About 1495.
Oil on pine panel.
H. 60⅜″, W. 37″; H. 61″, W. 36¾″.
Gift of the Samuel H. Kress Foundation.
61.44.21, 22.

These paintings are two of eight panels of a retable evidently painted on the occasion of the marriages of two of the children of Ferdinand and Isabella, King and Queen of Spain, to the children of the Emperor Maximilian I and Mary of Burgundy.

This unidentified painter displays a familiarity with the work of Rogier van der Weyden, perhaps the most influential of the Flemish painters. The crumpled, tubular drapery folds, the odd half-crouched stance of the Archangel, the solemn faces with their large eyes, and the detailed miniature landscapes in the background are all characteristic of

Rogier. The iconography of the *Annunciation* is
unusual in that the forthcoming birth of Christ
is symbolized by the Christ child, cross in arms and
preceded by the Holy Ghost, coming to earth on
rays emanating from the mouth of God the Father.

RODRIGO DE OSONA THE YOUNGER.
Spanish, Valencian,
active late 15th–early 16th centuries.
The Adoration of the Magi.

Oil on wood panel.
H. 75¼″, W. 47¾″.
Gift of the Samuel H. Kress Foundation. 61.44.23.

It is known that Rodrigo the Elder had a son who was also a painter, because an *Adoration of the Magi* in the National Gallery, London, which this panel closely resembles, is signed "lo fil de mestre Rodrigo" (the son of Master Rodrigo). The figures and the imaginative landscape with atmospheric perspective show the strong Flemish influence that dominated Spanish art in this period. Rodrigo's insistence on faithfully portraying the smallest details, resulting in a cluttered composition, is characteristic of much Spanish art.

PIETER COECK VAN AELST.
Flemish, 1502-1550.
Saint Joseph of Arimathea *and*
Saint Mary Magdalen.

Wings from a triptych. Oil on wood panel.
H. 43″, W. 12¼″.
Gift of Mr. and Mrs. Charles R. Blyth. 50.13.

Pieter Coeck, a painter from Antwerp, was an
extremely versatile artist; in addition to painting,
engraving, and sculpting, he translated a book on
Vitruvius by the Bolognese architect Serlio. In this
picture he continues the late Flemish tradition
of exaggerated, eccentric landscapes, but he uses some
Italian elements of decoration that he may have
seen in his travels. He was the teacher of
Pieter Brueghel the Elder, who married his daughter.

HERRY MET DE BLES.
Flemish, 1480-1550.
Orpheus in Hades.

Oil on wood panel. H. 9⅛″, W. 11⅞″.
Gift of The de Young Museum Society. 51.23.1.

Orpheus, the mythological hero-king of Thrace, was renowned for his musical talents. Upon the death of his wife Eurydice he descended into Hades, the land of the dead, seeking to reclaim her. In this picture he is seen at the lower left, charming Cerberus, the guardian of the gate to the underworld; and again in the center, persuading Pluto and Persephone, rulers of Hades to release his wife. Upon leaving, he was told not to look back at her, but he did, whereupon she disappeared into the underworld forever.

Herry was a follower of the landscapist Patinier, but here he shows the influence of Hieronymus Bosch, one of the greatest masters of fantasy in the history of art. In this painting, the artist turns to a classical instead of a religious subject, reflecting the rise of Renaissance humanism in Flanders.

ATTRIBUTED TO JOACHIM PATINIER.

Flemish, about 1475-1524.

Saint Francis Receiving the Stigmata.

Oil on wood panel.
H. 16½″, W. 11¹¹⁄₁₆″.
Gift of Alvin J. Gordon. 54.34.

During his forty days of fasting and prayer in a mountain retreat, a vision of the crucified Christ appeared to Saint Francis and gave him the stigmata, the five wounds of Christ, which he bore for the rest of his life.

Patinier is considered one of the fathers of modern landscape painting; he frequently practised his specialty in collaboration with other painters, particularly Gerard David and Quentin Massys. He was one of the first to use atmospheric perspective, in which the depth of the scene is further emphasized by showing a bluish haze in the distant background.

JOOS VAN CLEVE.
Flemish, Antwerp, about 1485-1540.
Lucretia.

Oil on wood panel. H. 29⅞″, W. 23⅞″.
Gift of The M. H. de Young Endowment Fund.
54651.

Lucretia was a noble Roman lady who, after being raped by Sextus Tarquinius, demanded an oath of vengeance from her husband and her father, and then killed herself. In the Renaissance such moralizing legends from antiquity frequently supplanted the Christian parables of the Middle Ages.

Joos van Cleve was a contemporary of Holbein, Massys, and Mabuse, and the portraits attributed to him share the smooth, accomplished style of these masters. Another version of our Lucretia is in the Kunsthistorische Museum, Vienna.

FLEMISH, ANTWERP, ABOUT 1530.
Adoration of the Shepherds.

Oil on wood panel.
H. 30¾″, W. 24¾″.
Purchased by the City and County of San Francisco.
47.6.

In this painting the artist has increased the drama and emotion of the scene by placing it in a nocturnal setting and flooding it with an unearthly light emanating from the Christ child, with the excited gestures and wildly fluttering drapery further heightening the effect. Few of the Antwerp Mannerists can be specifically identified.

FLEMISH, ANTWERP, ABOUT 1520.
Triptych: Adoration of the Magi
(*central panel*), Adoration of the Shepherds
(*left wing*), The Presentation of Christ
at the Temple (*right wing*).

Oil on wood panel.
H. 40½″, W. 27⅜″; H. 40⅛″, W. 12″;
H. 40⅛″, W. 12⅛″.
Gift of Mrs. Betty Walter Sirigo. 57.17.2 A, B, C.

At the beginning of the sixteenth century the center
of Flemish painting shifted from Bruges to
Antwerp. Some of the artists there became influenced
by Italian Mannerism, which they adapted to their
indigenous style. This influence is seen here
in the Renaissance architecture, the fanciful costumes
and armaments, and in the elegant, theatrical
poses of the figures.

ATTRIBUTED TO JAN VERMEYEN.
Dutch, 1500–1559.

Portrait of a Prelate.

Oil on wood panel.
H. 28½", W. 21½".
Gift of the Roscoe and Margaret Oakes Foundation.
65–20–1.

This portrait of a stern man of the church (holding the biretta of his office), believed to be a Bishop of Rochester, was a century ago attributed to Hans Holbein, and more recently to Cornelis van Cleve. While the question is still open to discussion, the current attribution serves to bring us closer to the identity of the author of a group of portraits of which this is an outstanding example.

JAKOB SEISENEGGER.

Austrian, 1505-1567.

Portrait of a Nobleman.

Oil on canvas.
H. 46″, W. 34¾″.
Gift of the Samuel H. Kress Foundation. 61.44.33.

Seisenegger was a painter to the court of King Ferdinand I, who later became Emperor of the Holy Roman Empire. He is best known for his portraits, especially those of members of the Habsburg family. In 1532, in Bologna, he painted a full-length portrait of Charles V which Titian used as a model for his portrait a year later.

LUCAS CRANACH THE YOUNGER.
German, Saxon, 1515-1586.

Portrait of a Man.

Dated 1545
Oil on parchment stretched on wood panel.
H. 12½", W. 9⅞".
Gift of the M. H. de Young Endowment Fund.
43.9.3.

Lucas Cranach succeeded his illustrious father as
court painter to the Elector of Saxony. He
is best known for his portraits with their precise
rendering of the textures of skin, hair, and clothing.

LUCAS CRANACH THE ELDER.
German, Saxon, 1472-1553.
Madonna and Child with the Infant Baptist
and Angels.

Signed with dragon cypher; dated 1545.
Oil on wood panel.
H. 47½", W. 28⅞".
Gift of Mr. and Mrs. Richard S. Rheem. 46.4.

In his early years Cranach worked in Austria, painting religious subjects in which the landscape plays a vital role, revealing a connection with the ideas of the Danube School. In 1505 Frederick the Wise of Saxony summoned Cranach to his court, where his style changed considerably. There he painted numerous representations of the worldly, graceful figures of the aristocratic society for which he worked—not only as court painter but also as designer for court functions.

EL GRECO.
(Domenikos Theotokópoulos).
Spanish, born in Crete, 1541-1614.
Saint Francis Venerating the Crucifix.

*About 1595. Signed: "domenikos theotokópoulos
e'poíei." Oil on canvas.
H. 58", W. 41½".
Gift of the Samuel H. Kress Foundation. 61.44.24.*

Saint Francis is revering the crucifix which leans on a
skull, a reminder of Golgotha (literally, place of
skulls), or Calvary, and of the transience of all
earthly things.

El Greco was evidently first trained in his native
Crete by an artist still painting in the Byzantine
tradition. About 1560 he went to Venice and learned
from Titian and Tintoretto; then he proceeded to
Rome and saw the works of Raphael, Michelangelo,
and the central Italian Mannerists. In 1576 he
settled in Toledo for the rest of his life. One of the
most individualistic artists of all time, El Greco turned
his knowledge of the somewhat superficial Mannerist
style towards the intensifying of religious
mysticism. His spiritual fervor reflects the mood of
the Counter Reformation, which reached the
height of intensity in Spain.

EL GRECO.

(Domenikos Theotokópoulos).
Spanish, born in Crete, 1541-1614.

Saint John the Baptist.

*About 1600. Signed: "domenikos theotokópoulos
e'poíei." Oil on canvas.
H. 43¾", W. 26".
Purchased with funds from various donors. 46.7.*

This painting demonstrates the qualities which have
made El Greco a cardinal figure in the history of
art. Highly regarded in his own time, he was
afterwards considered a minor eccentric until the late
nineteenth century. The languidly posed,
elongated figure with slender, attenuated limbs and
hands, the shimmering, silvery light that
pervades the scene, the violently turbulent sky—
all create the impression of intense religious fervor.

PETER PAUL RUBENS.
Flemish, Antwerp, 1577-1640.
The Tribute Money.

About 1612. Oil on wood panel. H. 56½″, W. 74¾″.
Purchased with funds from various donors. 44.11.

Rubens was the most prominent master of Baroque
painting. As court painter and unofficial envoy of
the Spanish Regent of Flanders, he travelled to
Holland, Spain, and England, combining diplomacy
with commissions for painting. In the history of
art there is no artist more versatile and prolific than
Rubens. His works include altarpieces, decorations
for palaces and processions, hunting scenes, portraits,
tapestry designs, and book illustrations.

This painting represents the moment when
Christ confounds the priests of the Temple of
Jerusalem, who hoped to trap him into denying
Rome's authority to collect tribute money. Christ,
pointing to Caesar's image on a coin, said "Render
therefore unto Caesar the things which be Caesar's,
and unto God the things which be God's."

JACOB JORDAENS.
Flemish, 1593-1678.
The Holy Family.

*Signed: "J. Jor Fe." About 1620. Oil on linden wood
panel. H. 48½″, W. 36⅞″.
Gift of Samuel H. Kress. 55279.*

A contemporary of Rubens, Jordaens has been called
"the Caravaggio of Flanders." The figures in this
composition are closely crowded and are strongly lit
by a raking light leaving deep shadows—both
primary elements in Caravaggio's style. The figures
themselves, especially the cherubic Christ child,
reveal the strong influence of Rubens. Jordaen's style
was very popular in his time; his paintings were
sought after throughout Europe.

ATTRIBUTED TO
PETER PAUL RUBENS.
Flemish, 1577–1640.
Archduke Albert of Austria.

Oil on copper.
H. 3⅞″, W. 2⅞″.
Gift of The de Young Museum Society.
52–6–5.

The suggestion that this exceptionally fine yet powerful miniature portrait, at first attributed to the Dutch painter Frans Pourbus the Younger, might be a very early work by Rubens has been advanced by some scholars. It is believed that the painting was done by Rubens prior to his sojourn in Italy (1600–1608), perhaps on the occasion of the marriage of the Archduke to the Infanta Isabella of Spain in 1598.

CORNEILLE DE LYON.
French, about 1500-1575.
Portrait of a Man.

Oil on wood panel.
H. 6¼″, W. 5″.
Gift of The Auxiliary of The de Young Museum
Society. 62.12.2.

Corneille, born in The Hague, was a painter to the royal court of Henry II, even though he lived in Lyon. His portraits are closer to miniature painting than to easel painting. Most of his subjects were members of the king's court, as this gentleman probably was. He wears black in the Spanish mode, a style of dress widely copied throughout Europe in the sixteenth century. This may be observed in other portraits of this period illustrated here.

PETER PAUL RUBENS.
Flemish, Antwerp, 1577-1640.

Pair of Portraits.

Rogier Clarisse and his Wife, Sara Breyll.

Dated 1611. Oil on wood panel.
H. 46½″, W. 36¾″; H. 46½″, W. 36³⁄₁₆″.
Gift of Roscoe and Margaret Oakes; Gift of
Ben N. Maltz. 53.12; 60.27.

In spite of his experience in Italy, Rubens retained features of his native Flemish painting which may be seen in these portraits. The faithful rendering of every detail, the delight in accurately portraying the various textures of skin, hair and beard, clothing and fur, and the quietly expressive faces and hands are in the tradition of earlier Flemish portraiture.

PETER PAUL RUBENS.
Flemish, 1577-1640 (figures).
JAN BRUEGHEL THE ELDER.
Flemish, 1568-1625 (setting).
Christ Appears to Saint Mary Magdalen
after His Resurrection.

Oil on wood panel. H. 22⅝″, W. 36½″.
Gift of The de Young Museum Society. 49.6.

These two paintings are further examples of the
not uncommon practice in this period of collaboration
between two artists on one work. In the first
work (*Noli Me Tangere*) Rubens painted the figures
while Brueghel painted the exquisite setting with
the touch that earned him the nickname "Velvet"
Brueghel. The two painters were close friends.
Brueghel was not the only artist to work with Rubens;
Frans Snyders frequently painted the animals in
Rubens' pictures. In the *Feast of the Gods* the figures
were painted by Hans Rottenhammer, a German
painter of historical and mythological subjects
to the court of the Emperor Rudolph II. He was in
Italy studying the works of Titian and Veronese
from about 1595 to 1606, where he met Brueghel;
therefore we can assume that this gathering of
the gods was painted during that time.

HANS ROTTENHAMMER.
German, 1564-1625 (figures).
JAN BRUEGHEL THE ELDER.
Flemish, 1568-1625 (setting).
Feast of the Gods.

About 1600. Oil on copper. H. 18¾″, W. 26⅝″.
Purchased with funds from various donors. 62.31.

JOACHIM BEUCKELAER.
Flemish, about 1533-1573.
Market Place.

Signed: "J B 1565." Oil on wood panel.
H. 33¼", W. 44¾".
Purchased by the City and County of San Francisco.
54.21.

Beuckelaer, a native of Antwerp, studied there with Pieter Aertsen who was the husband of his aunt. He followed his master in his choice of subjects: religious pictures (most of which were destroyed by the Iconoclasts), market and kitchen scenes which often contain religious subjects in the background, and peasant genre. Beuckalaer sold his pictures for small sums and died in poverty. Shortly afterwards, it is recorded, his prices had risen ten times over—a not unfamiliar episode in the history of art.

JEAN COURTNEYS.
French, Limoges, 1546-1586.
Platter.

About 1570. Enameled copper.
L. 20½″, W. 14½″.
Gift of Mr. and Mrs. George Wagner. 48.2.

The subject represented by this important enameler
is the Passage of the Israelites through the Red
Sea. The technique of enamel painting was
developed in Europe about A.D. 1500 and is quite
distinct from *cloisonné* and *champlevé* enameling,
which had been known for many centuries.

In painting with enamel, the entire object to be
enameled is covered, back and front, with a layer of
dark-colored enamel and is then fired. Over this
dark ground the subject is painted in white enamel in
varying thicknesses. In the thinly painted areas
the translucency of the white enamel permits some of
the dark ground to show through and thus modify
the white. Where the white is applied thickly
the dark ground is completely obscured. In this way
the enamel painter is able to model his forms by
light and shade, except that in the platter shown here
he paints in the lights rather than the shadows,
and a third firing was necessary to add the flesh tones.

ANTHONY VAN DYCK.
Flemish, 1599-1641.

Portrait of a Lady.

About 1620. Oil on canvas. H. 57¾″, W. 42¾″.
The Roscoe and Margaret Oakes Foundation. L 58.6.

The son of a wealthy, cultured family, van Dyck was an apprentice in the studio of Henrik van Balen. In 1617 he entered Rubens' atelier and was quickly acknowledged the most brilliant of the many famous pupils and collaborators there. Afterwards, aside from two brief periods when he lived in Antwerp, his birthplace, he achieved his greatest fame abroad: in Italy, particularly in Genoa, and in England, as court painter to Charles I. This portrait, painted with the utmost sensitivity, delicacy, and sympathy with the sitter, was done near the end of van Dyck's first Antwerp period, about 1620. It shares characteristics with other van Dyck portraits of the period, especially the beautiful *Margaretha Snyders* in the Frick Collection, New York.

ANTHONY VAN DYCK.
Flemish, 1599-1641.

Marie-Claire, Duchess d'Havré, and Child.

Signed: "Caval° A. van Dyck F A 1634."
Oil on canvas.
H. 82⅛″, W. 48⅝″.
Gift of Roscoe and Margaret Oakes. 58.43.

This portrait belongs to the third period of van Dyck's activity in his native Flanders. He devised this type of double portrait, of a grown woman accompanied by a child or dwarf, as a pleasing combination of dignity and animation to gratify his patrician patrons of Genoa, Antwerp, and London. Van Dyck, more than any other painter, laid the foundation for the great school of portrait painting that bloomed in eighteenth-century England.

CORNELIS DE VOS.
Flemish, 1585-1651.
Pair of Portraits: A Man *and* A Woman.

Man's portrait inscribed: "Aetatis Suae. 73 Anno.
1632." Oil on wood panel.
H. 50⅜″, W. 38¾″; H. 48¾″, W. 37″.
Gift of Mr. and Mrs. Hermann Schuelein.
47.15; 46.12.

Cornelis de Vos was born in Hulst. In 1659 he
was a pupil of David Remeeus in Antwerp, where
he spent most of his life. Vos was a brother-in-law
of the well known painter Frans Snyders. He
worked often under Rubens and through Rubens
received commissions for painting portraits. The
relationship between these two artists was like that
between Titian and Moroni. In addition to his
painting career, Cornelis de Vos also enjoyed
success as an art dealer.

CORNELIS DE VOS.
Flemish, 1585-1651.
Portrait of a Lady with her Daughter.

Oil on pine panel.
H. 43½″, W. 33⅞″.
Gift of the Samuel H. Kress Foundation. 61.44.34.

GEORGES DE LA TOUR.

French, 1593-1652.

Old Peasant *and* Peasant Woman.

Oil on canvas.
H. 35⅞″, W. 23⅝″; H. 35⅞″, W. 23⅝″.
The Roscoe and Margaret Oakes Foundation.
L 56.13.1; L 56.13.2.

One of the most individualistic painters in the history of French art, La Tour shared Caravaggio's belief in naturalism and the power of light to influence emotion. He was chiefly a genre painter, expressing religious subjects in terms of simple peasant scenes. His figures have a solid, sculptural quality emphasized by their natural yet graceful gestures, a strong raking light, and, as in these paintings, by their placement in simple architectural settings suggesting sculpture placed in niches. La Tour's paintings have sincere emotions and a deep sense of human dignity, in contrast with the frequently humorous quality of contemporary Dutch genre painting.

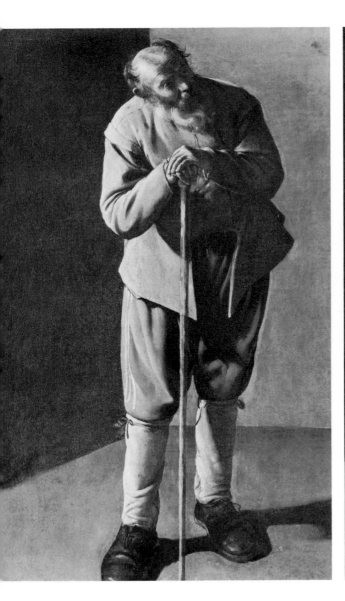

NICOLAS POUSSIN.
French, 1594-1665.

The Israelites Worshipping the Golden Calf.

Signed: "N. P. 1629." Oil on canvas.
H. 39⅛", W. 50⅝".
Gift of the Samuel H. Kress Foundation. 61.44.30.

Although Poussin spent virtually all of his career in Rome, he was the dominant force in seventeenth century French painting. The supreme classicist, he had a highly rational, intellectual approach to his work; once he wrote to a friend that the highest purpose of painting is to represent noble, significant human actions. Events should be portrayed in an ideal fashion; not as they actually may have happened, but as they would have happened in a perfectly ordered world. Thus, figures would react in a predictable, logical manner, giving Poussin's work a calculated style appealing more to the mind than to the senses.

PAUL BRILL.
Flemish, 1554–1626.

Classical Landscape (Pan Pursuing Syrinx).

Oil on canvas.
H: 19″, W. 27¾″.
Purchased by the City and County of San Francisco.
49–11.

Paul Brill and his elder brother Mattheus were
specialists in the art of landscape painting. They
were born in Antwerp, but each of them went to
Rome at approximately the age of twenty. There they
painted large fresco compositions in the Vatican
and other churches and palaces, which form
the link between the views of Patinier and Brueghel
and the ideal landscape brought to perfection by
Poussin and Claude. Paul, who was also an
engraver, is best known for small easel pictures
such as this one.

CLAUDE GELLÉE, CALLED CLAUDE LORRAINE.
French, 1600-1682.
Classical Landscape with Figures at Sunset.

About 1640. Oil on canvas.
H. 38⅛", W. 52".
Gift of the Samuel H. Kress Foundation. 61.44.31.

Claude spent most of his life in Rome where his work was much in demand among collectors. He specialized in landscapes, in which the figures are merely incidental to the composition. His idyllic scenes emphasize the serenity of the natural world with man in proper relationship to it. In this carefully arranged composition the architecture is fitted into the landscape in a manner suggesting an ideal existence, in which man lives in harmony rather than in conflict with nature. Claude was especially interested in the effects of light; in many of his paintings the light comes from the background and the scene is often bathed in the hazy, luminous atmosphere of early morning or late afternoon. His landscapes exerted a wide influence; they were well known to Watteau and Fragonard.

113

SPANISH, ABOUT 1600.
Vargueño (portable desk) and Stand.

Walnut, ebony, ivory, iron, and velvet.
H. 28⅝″, W. 34¾″, D. 16½″.
Gift of William Randolph Hearst. 47.20.1.

This is a characteristically Spanish type of desk. The exterior, as in Spanish houses, is comparatively plain except for areas reserved for ornamental enrichment: the lock, the handles, and the pierced and gilt wrought-iron fittings mounted over red velvet. The interior provides a striking contrast with its gilded splendor and architectural design executed in ebony, ivory, and gilded wood and iron. The stand, with its shell-terminated pulls on which the desk rests, is much restored.

MARCOS COVARRUBIAS.

Spanish, Toledo, about 1550.

Embroidered Altar Frontal.

Silk and metal thread on velvet.
H. 41", L. 90".
Gift of the estate of Frederick Talbot. 50727.

Worked chiefly in the *appliqué* and couching techniques, this altar frontal was executed to the order of Charles V for the Church of San Juan de los Reyes in Toledo. In the large roundels are represented St. Paul, the Lamb of God held by an Angel, and St. Jerome. The smaller roundels depict scenes from the lives of Christ and the Saints. By the end of the sixteenth century Spanish artists and craftsmen such as Covarrubias had thoroughly assimilated the Italian Renaissance style as is shown in this embroidery where Renaissance motifs are used exclusively.

JAN STEEN.
Dutch, about 1626-1679.
The Marriage Contract (The Marriage
of Tobias).

Signed: "J. STEEN." Oil on canvas.
H. 41", W. 50⅛".
Gift of The de Young Museum Society. 62.12.1.

This scene, part of the Old Testament story of the
journey of Tobias with the Archangel Raphael,
portrays the signing of the marriage contract between
the young man and his bride, Sara. Steen, best
known for his narrative genre paintings, has
transformed the Biblical subject into a lively
representation of Dutch home life.

ESAIAS VAN DE VELDE.
Dutch, 1591–1630 (figures).
BARTHOLOMEUS VAN BASSEN.
Dutch, about 1590-1652 (architectural setting).
Lazarus at the Rich Man's Door.

Oil on wood panel. H. 20⅛″, W. 26½″.
Purchased by the City and County of San Francisco.
51.4.4.

This picture is evidence of the high degree of specialization that developed in Dutch painting at this period; collaboration on a picture, with each artist working within his specialty, was quite common. The Biblical subject is treated as a genre scene, taking place in the home of a wealthy burgher.

117

ENGLISH, EXETER, 1590.

Paneled Room.

Oak.
L. 27', W. 19'2", H. 9'2".
Gift of Mrs. E. John Magnin. 46.19.

This is a typical English domestic interior of the late Tudor period. Rooms were "sealed" (against drafts) by lining the walls with wooden panels. During the Tudor period these linings were made up of many small rectangular oak panels held together by a grid of rails and stiles which were joined by a system of mortises and tenons secured by wooden pegs. The plaster ceiling, which is a reproduction, is typical of the period. The system of ribs has its origin in the groin ribs of medieval vaulting except that here they have been adapted to a flat surface. The brass chandelier is mid-seventeenth century Dutch.

FRENCH, ABOUT 1550.
Frame.

Boxwood.
H. 21″, W. 14¼″.
Gift of George Wagner. 45.27.

Hard, fine-grained boxwood lends itself to delicate carving and is often used for small sculptures. In the style of the Renaissance, this frame is typically French in the subtle variations employed by its skilled carver. There is also a pleasant contrast and proportion between the richly carved areas and those ornamented only with moldings.

DUTCH, ABOUT 1650.
Armoire.

Oak and ebony.
H. 84¼", W. 69".
Gift of Miss Carlotta Mabury. 55281.

The tall two-door cupboard was a creation of the seventeenth century. In this restrained Dutch Baroque example one sees a survival of a quiet Renaissance architectural treatment with its arches, pilasters, and cornices. The introduction of dark-faceted moldings and panels and the large ball feet are the chief Baroque elements in the design. The tops of such pieces were commonly used to display Delft ware. A similar cabinet is represented in our Pieter de Hooch (page 133).

REMBRANDT VAN RIJN.
Dutch, 1606-1669.
Joris de Caullery.

Signed: "RHL van Ryn 1632." Oil on canvas.
H. 40⅜", W. 33".
The Roscoe and Margaret Oakes Foundation.
L 55.47.

It is documented that in 1654 Joris de Caullery, a
ship's captain and later a wine merchant and
innkeeper at The Hague, gave his daughter a portrait
of himself holding a musket. As this is the only
known Rembrandt portrait with such an accessory,
it is very likely the painting mentioned in the
document. It was done one year after Rembrandt
moved to Amsterdam, when he was reaching
the height of popularity as a portraitist. In this early
period Rembrandt, more than his contemporaries, was
fond of dramatic, forceful poses, as in this picture of
a vigorous, self-assured burgher.

REMBRANDT VAN RIJN.
Dutch, 1606-1669.

Self-Portrait of the Artist Sketching.

Signed: ". . . brandt 1653." Oil on canvas.
H. 29", W. 24¼".
The Roscoe and Margaret Oakes Foundation. L 56.3.

This self-portrait was painted in Rembrandt's later years, long after he had lost the favor of the wealthy patrons of Amsterdam. Another version of this composition is in Dresden. Rembrandt shows in his portraits a deep psychological insight which is no less penetrating when applied to himself. Here he is the master of *chiaroscuro,* with the deep shadows permitting him to stress the essential quality of the subject. He was interested in painting people of character, particularly those who had overcome sorrow and had reached a philosophical adjustment to life; this portrait reminds us of these qualities of Rembrandt's own life.

FRANS HALS.
Dutch, about 1581-1666.
The Cavalier in White.

About 1630. Oil on canvas. H. 26½″, W. 22½″.
The Roscoe and Margaret Oakes Foundation.
L 55.45.

Hals reached the height of his renown in the 1630's, when this picture was painted. In this period his figures are finely drawn with great plasticity and brilliant coloring. Hals, a shrewd observer of character, was especially interested in hearty, robust people like himself, painting them with unequalled vividness.

BARENT FABRITIUS.
Dutch, 1624-1673.
Hagar Leaving Abraham.

Oil on canvas. H. 42¾″, W. 42¾″.
Anonymous gift. 50.34.

Fabritius was a pupil of Rembrandt, whom he greatly admired. In this painting his style is close to Rembrandt's in its infusion of the Old Testament subject with sadness and pathos, and in the historically correct dress of the figures.

GERBRAND VAN DEN EECKHOUT.
Dutch, 1621-1674.

Saint Peter Healing the Lame.

Signed: F. v. d. EECKHOUT f. Ao 1667.
Oil on canvas. H. 24½″, W. 27⅜″.
Gift of Mr. and Mrs. George T. Cameron. 47.7.

Eeckhout was one of very few of Rembrandt's followers who never abandoned the master's style. In this Biblical illustration he is particularly close to Rembrandt, as seen in his use of light and shadow to express the mystery and drama of the miracle taking place. Deep shadows fill the background while all attention is focused on the main figures, bathed in a warm, soft glow highlighting their expressions and gestures.

ABRAHAM DANIELSZ HONDIUS.
Dutch, about 1635-1695.
The Annunciation to the Shepherds.

Oil on wood panel.
H. 15¼″, W. 19″.
Gift of Mr. and Mrs. Robert Neuhaus in Memory of
Louise Ann Neuhaus, Mother of Mr. Neuhaus.
52.14.

Hondius was best known for his highly naturalistic
animal paintings, a skill evident in this picture.
The religious subject here is portrayed as an amusing
barnyard genre scene, with an unexpected Italian
touch in the Baroque angel floating down to earth.

JACOB VAN OOST THE YOUNGER.
Flemish, 1639-1713.
Mercury and Jupiter in the House of
Philemon and Baucis.

Oil on canvas. H. 65⅜″, W. 92¼″.
Gift of Dr. Rudolf J. Heinemann. 46.14.

When Jupiter and Mercury visited the land of
Phrygia a poor couple, Philemon and Baucis, were
the only ones in their village to offer the gods,
disguised as humans, food and shelter for the night.
The gods removed the old couple to safety and
punished the village for its selfishness by flooding it.
They then rewarded Philemon and Baucis for
their generosity by transforming their house into a
temple, of which they became priest and priestess.
This Roman legend is comparable to the stories
of Abraham and Noah.

JOOS DE MOMPER.

Flemish, 1564-1635.

The Valley.

Oil on wood panel. H. 25½″, W. 41½″.
Purchased by the City and County of San Francisco.
55.13.

Joos de Momper was a landscape painter active in Antwerp. Jan Brueghel and other important artists frequently provided the figures for his scenes. He is noted for his hilly landscapes which reveal the surviving influence of the mannered, often imaginary landscapes of the late Flemish primitives such as Joachim Patinier and Herri Met de Bles.

PHILIPS DE KONINCK.
Dutch, 1619-1688.
Entrance to a Forest.

Signed: "P Koninck." Oil on canvas.
H. 52½", W. 62½".
Gift of the M. H. de Young Endowment Fund.
43.9.2.

Koninck first studied painting under his brother Jacob, and under Rembrandt in Amsterdam. He painted a great variety of subjects, but specialized in bold, sweeping landscapes bathed in a strong light.

JAN VAN GOYEN.
Dutch, 1596-1656.
The Thunderstorm.

Signed: "I VGoyen 1641." Oil on canvas.
H. 53⅞", W. 72".
Purchased by the City and County of San Francisco.
48.7.

Van Goyen studied with several masters, including
Esaias van de Velde. He traveled widely. Numerous
sketches of foreign landscapes by him have
survived. He became one of the most outstanding
Dutch landscapists, with his strong feeling of
atmosphere heightening the realism and intensity
of his paintings.

SALOMON VAN RUYSDAEL.
Dutch, about 1600-1670.
River View of Nymwegen with the Valkhof.

Signed: "S Ruysdael 1648." Oil on canvas.
H. 40¾", W. 56¾".
Gift of the Samuel H. Kress Foundation. 61.44.36.

The rivers of Holland, as well as the sea, were of primary importance in Dutch life. They were the main avenues of transportation and freighting throughout the country; also, they were the most readily available source of irrigation. This painting was probably commissioned or purchased by a merchant who plied these waters.

GERRIT BERCKHEYDE.
Dutch, 1638-1698.
The Singel at Amsterdam.

Signed: "Gerrit Berckheyde." Oil on canvas.
H. 20¾", W. 24¼".
Gift of Mr. and Mrs. Clinton L. Walker. 55.18.

Cityscapes were popular in the seventeenth century Netherlands; their intimacy and precision follow the tradition of the little scenes beyond the windows in the backgrounds of the Flemish primitives of two hundred years before.

PIETER DE HOOCH.
Dutch, 1629-about 1683.
Young Mother.

About 1663. Signed: "P. d HOOCH." Oil on canvas.
H. 26⅝", W. 21¹³⁄₁₆".
Gift of the Samuel H. Kress Foundation. 61.44.37.

At his best, Pieter de Hooch is second only to Vermeer in his depiction of serene interiors and the light which pervades them. He was one of the most prominent genre painters of the seventeenth century Dutch school. Born in Rotterdam, he studied there under Nicolas Berchem; later he worked in Delft, Leyden, The Hague, and Amsterdam.
Many of the pictures of his early period, such as this one, show charming scenes of family life in simple surroundings. Later he did more elegant and fashionable paintings less suited to his gifts and temperament.

133

GERARD TERBORCH.
Dutch, 1617-1681.
Gentleman in Black.

Signed: "GTB." Oil on copper. H. 19½", W. 14¾".
Gift of Mr. and Mrs. George T. Cameron. 52.31.

Terborch learned to paint from his father and from Pieter Molijn. Later, he travelled widely in England, Germany, and Italy for several years. Delighting in the depiction of rich materials, Terborch was one of the greatest Dutch masters in intimate genre pictures representing the daily life of the upper classes. He is also noted for his finely finished small-scale portraits.

DAVID TENIERS THE YOUNGER.

Flemish, 1610-1690.

Peasant Walking.

Signed: "D. TENIERS. Fe." Oil on wood panel.
H. 10⅜", W. 8⅛".
Gift of Mrs. Herbert Fleishhacker. 45.33.1

Teniers learned painting from his father, David Teniers the Elder, and was strongly influenced by Rubens and Brouwer. He became a Master in the Antwerp Guild in 1633, and later, in Brussels, was court painter and gallery director to the Archduke Leopold Wilhelm. He painted several views of the Archduke's gallery in which the actual pictures, though tiny in scale, may be identified today. He is noted for his genre scenes populated with amusing, frequently caricatured, peasant types.

GABRIEL METSU.
Dutch, 1629-1667.
Reverie (Woman Playing the Viola da Gamba).
Signed: "G. METSU 1663." Oil on wood panel.
H. 17⁵⁄₁₆″, W. 14³⁄₁₆″.
Gift of Roscoe and Margaret Oakes. 60.30.

A pupil of Gerard Dou and strongly influenced by Rembrandt, Metsu worked primarily in Leiden and Amsterdam. He specialized in cheerful, graceful scenes of upper class life. His paintings are usually small in scale, brilliantly colored, and exquisitely finished, as is this panel with its shimmering silk drapery.

DAVID TENIERS THE YOUNGER.
Flemish, 1610-1690.
Music Party.

Signed: "D. TENIERS. FEC." Oil on canvas.
H. 14", W. 10¼".
Gift of The M. H. de Young Endowment Fund.
54652.

Dutch genre painting was intended not merely for
decorative effect, but for intimate contemplation
by the burghers as a pleasant reminder of the serene
lives they led. The patrons, representative of a
pragmatic middle class, generally preferred pictures
reflecting their everyday lives to compositions
in the "grand manner" of the Baroque. There
was much variety in genre painting, each artist usually
catering to the taste and means of a certain level
of society. This may readily be observed by
comparing Teniers' tavern scene with Metsu's
elegant young lady practising at home.
(See opposite page.)

JAN BRUEGHEL THE ELDER.
Flemish, 1568-1625.
Flower Still-Life.

Oil on wood panel. H. 10½", W. 7½".
Gift of Mrs. Herbert Fleishhacker. 47.4.3.

The son of Pieter Brueghel the Elder, Jan was a
famous and wealthy painter in his time. Much
of his work was done for the Archduke Albert and
the Infanta Isabella. Flowers, birds and animals,
and objects in their collections frequently occur in
his paintings. He is known as "Velvet" Brueghel, as
his initial training in miniature painting gave his
work an unsurpassed delicacy of execution
and beauty of color.

JACOB VAN HULSDONCK.
Flemish, 1582-1647.
Fruit and Flowers.

Oil on wood panel. H. 19″, W. 24″.
Purchased by the City and County of San Francisco.
54.23.

Hulsdonck worked all his life in Antwerp, specializing in still-life painting. There is a striking difference between the severe arrangement of the separate elements of this picture and the sophisticated, seemingly casual, disarray of the still-life compositions on the following pages, illustrating a marked change in style halfway through the seventeenth century. A basket such as this one is usually found in his works.

WILLIAM VAN AELST.
Dutch, about 1625-1688.
Flower Still-Life.

Signed: "Guill mo van Aelst 1663." Oil on canvas.
H. 26¾", W. 21½".
Gift of Dr. Hermann Schuelein. 51.21.

Born in Delft, van Aelst was a pupil of his uncle, Evert van Aelst, whose style he followed. After seven years of working in Italy he settled in Amsterdam to commence still-life painting. His works were greatly admired in their day for their meticulous finish. There is an identical version of this picture, from the collection of King Willem V, in the Mauritshuis in The Hague.

ABRAHAM VAN BEYEREN.
Dutch, 1621-1675.
Still-Life.

Signed: "A B f 1666." Oil on canvas. H. 55", W. 46".
Gift of The de Young Museum Society. 51.23.2.

During the course of the seventeenth century, the style of Dutch still-life pictures grew increasingly lavish and complicated. None was more so than that of van Beyeren, who worked chiefly in The Hague and Delft. Such an assemblage of elaborate plate and produce on a table top is the domestic equivalent of the full Baroque religious or historical composition.

GERARD VAN OPSTAL.
Flemish, 1597-1668.
The Infant Hercules and the Serpent.

Ivory. H. 3½".
Gift of The de Young Museum Society. 52.6.4.

Van Opstal was an important Flemish ivory carver who, in 1621, was brought by Cardinal Richelieu to Paris, where he spent most of his life.

FRENCH, ABOUT 1650.
Cabinet and Stand.

Ebony, various inlays, and gilt bronze.
H. 7'6", W. 7'2½", D. 30".
Gift of William Randolph Hearst. 47.20.2.

Such monumental and sumptuously carved cabinets are characteristic of much of the furniture made in the vicinity of Paris for the French court. The scenes represented in the carvings are from the Old Testament, chiefly concerning the lives of David and Solomon. The central part of the interior is treated as a Renaissance architectural stage-setting with a group of gilt bronze statuettes enacting the Judgment of Solomon.

DITEL BRANSENHAUER.
Danish, died 1712.
Tankard.

About 1700. Marked: "$\frac{CL}{MW}$ DB." Silver.
H. 8¼", Diam. 5½".
Rupert Nelson Bequest, courtesy of the San Francisco Art Commission. 59.28.1.

The luxuriant foliate *repoussé* and chased decoration is typically Baroque in the vigorous movement with which the scrolling forms unfold. The three feet, the lion thumbpiece, and the coin set into the cover are characteristics of Scandinavian tankards. These large tankards were generally used as loving cups and were frequently pegged on the inside so that each of the participating drinkers could measure his portion.

GERMAN, AUGSBURG, ABOUT 1685.
Covered Porringer.

*Silver, engraved and gilded. Marks: "IW"
(unidentified); Augsburg pomegranate for ca. 1685.
H. 3⅝", Diam. 4⅞". Purchased by the City and
County of San Francisco. 51.4.3.*

Augsburg in the sixteenth and seventeenth centuries
was one of the most important trade and cultural
centers of northern Europe and boasted a host
of excellent craftsmen in many fields, among them
metalsmithing. Many of Europe's greatest goldsmiths
and armorers were situated in Augsburg. This
porringer is a typical example of the goldsmith's art
of the late Baroque period with its vigorous
scrollwork in both the applied and the engraved
ornament.

JAN FYT.
Flemish, 1611-1661.
Fruit and Game.

Signed: "JOANNES FYT." Oil on oak panel.
H. 29⅛", W. 43¾".
Gift of the Samuel H. Kress Foundation. 61.44.35.

Fyt learned his trade of painting still life and animal pictures from Franz Snyders, the associate of Rubens. He was born in Antwerp and became a master in the Antwerp Guild in 1630. He traveled in France and Italy before returning to his homeland. His virtuoso technique in the rendering of animal fur and the plumage of birds has seldom been surpassed.

SCHOOL OF LUCA FORTE.
Italian, Neapolitan, about 1650.
Fruit Still-Life.

Oil on canvas.
H. 22½", W. 29".
Gift of The de Young Museum Society. 58.48.2.

The Neapolitan school of still-life painting was dominated by the influences of Caravaggio and the Dutch school.

MASSIMO STANZIONE.
Italian, Neapolitan, 1585-1656.
Woman in Peasant Dress.

Signed: "EQ MAX." Oil on canvas.
H. 46¾", W. 38¼".
Gift of Archer M. Huntington. 41.1.2.

Stanzione, an artist of the Neapolitan school of the seventeenth century, was a pupil of Caracciolo and the master of Cavallino. He retained the dark, brooding quality (especially in his religious work) of his master, adding highlights of more brilliant color. The subject has such delicate features and a bearing so noble and gracious that it is possible she might have been a lady of higher birth who, for some reason, had attired herself in this colorful and richly embroidered peasant costume.

ATTRIBUTED TO PIETRO PAOLINI.
Italian, Tuscan, 1603–1681.

Young Man with a Butterfly.

Oil on canvas. H. 23¼″, W. 19″.
Gift of Mrs. Herbert Fleishhacker.
47–5–1.

Because of its strong chiaroscuro handling, this painting was formerly attributed to Caracciolo, a Neapolitan painter who, more than any other, absorbed the dark, vigorous style of Caravaggio and transformed it into a personal means of expression. More recently it has been suggested that this picture is more clearly related to the known works of Pietro Paolini, who was born a generation later in Lucca. Paolini went to Rome at an early age and became a pupil of Angelo Caroselli, who in turn followed Caravaggio.

149

PIER FRANCESCO MOLA.
Italian, Roman, 1612-1666.
Erminia and Vafrina Tending the
Wounded Tancred.

Oil on canvas.
H. 27⅛", W. 36⅛".
Gift of the Samuel H. Kress Foundation. 61.44.18.

This subject is an episode from the sixteenth-century epic poem, *Jerusalem Delivered,* by Torquato Tasso. The composition was influenced by a painting of the same subject by Nicolas Poussin now in the Hermitage, Leningrad. Mola spent several years in Venice where he absorbed much of the style of the High Renaissance Venetian masters. His work has a romantic quality that is appealing today but it was never really suited to the taste of the official patronage of Rome. His paintings were not appreciated until long after his death.

CARLOTTO (JOHANN CARL LOTH).
Italian (born in Munich), Venetian, 1632-1698.
The Meeting of Rebekah and
Abraham's Servant at the Well.

Oil on canvas. H. 54", W. 68".
Purchased by the City and County of San Francisco.
47.9.

Abraham sent his servant off to his native land,
Chaldea, to find a suitable wife for his son Isaac.
The servant prayed for guidance that the chosen
woman be the one who would give water to him and
his camels. His prayer was answered; at a well
he met Rebekah, who became Isaac's wife.

Loth, called Carlotto in Italy, was born in Munich
but received his training and worked all his life
in Venice, where he became one of the leading
masters of seventeenth-century Venetian painting.

GIOVANNI BATTISTA CARLONE.
Italian, Genoese, 1592-1677.

Saint Peter.

Signed: "G. Battista Carloni." Oil on canvas.
H. 38⅝″, W. 27⅜″.
Gift of Mrs. Frederick Rolandi. 46.15.

Early in the sixteenth century, the mercantile republic of Genoa became an oligarchy with all power in the hands of a few noble families. Much to the benefit of the arts, these families vied with one another in the splendor of their churches and palaces for which Carlone, with his brothers, painted numerous religious frescoes. The half length figure of an elderly male saint is a common theme in southern Baroque painting, especially in the works of Carlone's exact contemporary Ribera.

GUERCINO.
(GIOVANNI FRANCESCO BARBIERI).
Italian, Bolognese, 1591–1666.

Samson and the Honeycomb.

About 1657.
Oil on canvas. H. 39¾", W. 45¾".
Gift of The Roscoe and Margaret Oakes Foundation.
65.20.2.

Though born in Cento, a provincial town with no significant artistic tradition, Guercino rose to the first rank of seventeenth-century Italian painters. His brilliant early style, which involved strong contrasts of light and dark, was succeeded by a more classical style which conformed to the prevailing taste of Rome and Bologna. This painting is an excellent example of the rich color, sure technique, and breadth of conception which mark his very late period. There is documentary evidence that it was painted towards the end of 1657. It illustrates a legend taken from Chapter 14 of the Book of Judges in which Samson slays a lion and contracts a most unfortunate marriage. Guercino had treated this unusual subject once before (about 1625) in a painting done for the Barberini Family, which exists today in the Chrysler Collection.

CARLO MARATTA.
Italian, Roman, 1625–1713.

Marchioness Rospigliosi-Pallavicini.

Signed: "CM". Oil on canvas.
H. 30½", W. 25⅛".
Gift of the M. H. de Young Endowment Fund.
39.2.1.

Maratta enjoyed a long life and an unusually productive career. In contrast to Bacciccio, his only rival as the greatest painter in Rome during the last half of the 17th century, his art avoids the Maratta excitement of much Italian baroque art. Maratta never loses sight of the classical tradition which stems from Raphael, was revived by the Caracci and Domenichino, and reached him through his teacher Sacchi. After Bernini's death in 1680 it was this style, and Maratta as its chief exponent, that won the day. His portraits, of which this is a superb example, are equal to his religious works and appeal even more to contemporary taste.

BACCICCIO
(GIOVANNI BATTISTA GAULLI).
Italian, Genoese and Roman, 1639-1709.
The Adoration of the Lamb.

Oil on canvas. H. 25⅜″, W. 41¼″.
Gift of the M. H. de Young Endowment Fund.
54680.

This painting is a sketch for the fresco by Gaulli in the apsidal vault of the church of the Gesù in Rome, executed in the last quarter of the seventeenth century. Bacciccio learned from Van Dyck and Strozzi, and was popular in Genoa for his lively portraits. He went to Rome in 1657, where he came under the influence of Bernini. In his decorations for Il Gesù he employed Bernini's device of combining, at the edges of the composition, painted figures with relief figures modeled in stucco, giving the illusion of a celestial vision. Bacciccio's style, with wildly exuberant figures portrayed in every angle of foreshortening, was well suited to the splendor of the Baroque church.

GIOVANNI BATTISTA TIEPOLO.
Italian, Venetian, 1696-1770.
The Triumph of Flora.

About 1743. Oil on canvas.
H. 28¼″, W. 35″.
Gift of the Samuel H. Kress Foundation. 61.44.19.

Though he was the last of the great Venetian fresco painters, Tiepolo was such an international celebrity that we must seek out some of his finest works in such widely scattered places as Madrid, Würzburg, Udine and Milan. To a large extent he based his virtuoso art on a recreation of the style of his sixteenth century predecessor Veronese and his cool, silvery palette. Tiepolo achieved a balanced calm and an easy, flowing grace which, combined with his mastery of light and color, made his art the great culmination of Venetian painting. This picture was commissioned for Count Brühl (see page 200) and it has been suggested that the Neptune fountain in the background may be the same as the centerpiece of his porcelain Swan Service.

ANTONIO TARSIA.
Italian, Venetian, about 1663-1739.
Thetis.

About 1700. Terra cotta.
H. 11½", L. 16".
Gift of Mortimer Leventritt. 53.17.

Antonio Tarsia was a prominent Venetian sculptor
who produced many works for Venetian churches.
This terracotta sketch *(bozzetto)* is a study for the
marble version of this subject now in the Victoria and
Albert Museum, London. The motif of a reclining,
undraped figure with a flying scarf forming an
arc over the head goes back to classical antiquity and
was used by many European painters and sculptors
during the intervening centuries.

FRENCH, BEAUVAIS, ABOUT 1730.
Audience of the Oriental Prince.

Tapestry, silk and wool.
H. 10'3", W. 16'8".
Gift of the Roscoe and Margaret Oakes Foundation.
59.49.1.

This tapestry, an extraordinary example of the "chinoiserie" style, was woven after designs by Blin de Fontenay and Louis Vernansal. It is a delightful fantasy on life at the Chinese court which combines motifs from the Far East, Near East, and Europe. The narrow border woven to represent a gilt frame with acanthus carving is an innovation of the early eighteenth century dictated by changes in interior design which occurred at that time.

FRENCH, BEAUVAIS, ABOUT 1690.
Grotesques from the Italian Comedy Series.

Tapestry, silk and wool.
H. 9'7", W. 11'11".
Gift of the Roscoe and Margaret Oakes Foundation.
59.49.4.

A "grotesque" is a whimsical combination of human, animal, plant, and architectural elements in which fantasy has the upper hand. This series was woven after designs by Jean Berain and Jean-Baptiste Monnoyer at the French tapestry ateliers at Beauvais during the directorship of Phillipe Behagle. Also of interest in this set are the "chinoiserie" elements to be seen in the border designs.

The Beauvais workshops were established by Colbert to manufacture tapestries for private patrons while the Gobelins tapestry ateliers worked exclusively for the French state.

CHARLES ANTOINE COYSEVOX.
French, 1640-1720.
Self-Portrait.

About 1680. Terra cotta.
H. 27½″.
Gift of Mr. and Mrs. Grover Magnin. 47.19.

Coysevox was one of the most prolific sculptors of the *Grand Siècle*—the period of Louis XIV. He executed many works for Versailles and other royal residences. This self-portrait is typically Baroque in style. The almost arrogant confidence to be seen in the face is echoed in the tumultuous cascade of the curls of the wig and is further underlined by the bold diagonals in the agitated surface of the clothing and the angular turn of the head.

ANGELO DE' ROSSI.
Italian, 1671-1715.
Pope Alexander VIII (Pietro Ottoboni,
Pope 1689-1691).

Terra cotta.
H. 19".
Gift of the M. H. de Young Endowment Fund.
59.16.

This terracotta sketch (*bozzetto*) was a study for the bronze monument to Alexander VIII in St. Peter's, Rome. The spirit of the late Baroque work derives as much from the vigorous movement of the folds of the garments and the contrasting textures of their materials as it does from the facial features or the gesture of benediction.

EDMÉ BOUCHARDON.
French, 1698-1762.
Pope Clement XII (Lorenzo Corsini,
Pope 1730-40).

Terra cotta.
H. 29¾″.
Gift of the M. H. de Young Endowment Fund.
54899.

This important French sculptor was a pupil of
Guillaume Coustou. He lived for ten years in Rome
where he modeled this bust as a study for the
marble version in the Palazzo Corsini in Florence. It
was customary to make such clay sketches from
life as they could be modeled quickly in this highly
plastic material and could be later cast in bronze
or carved from marble. Often such terracotta
renderings are more lively and interesting than the
finished work as they reveal the direct and
spontaneous touch of the sculptor when he is closest
to his subject and material.

POLISH, KRAKOW, ABOUT 1750.
Chasuble.

Silk and metal thread.
H. 43″, W. 35″.
Gift of Archer M. Huntington. 16285.

This chasuble, produced at the Glaise workshops at Krakow, is unusual in that it is woven in the tapestry technique. The narrative part of the design concerns the history of Saint Stanislaus.

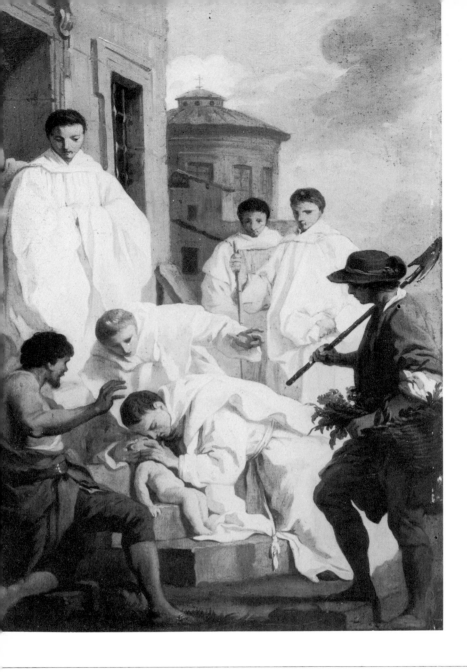

PIERRE SUBLEYRAS.
French, 1699-1749.
Saint Benedict Reviving a Dead Child.

Sketch for a painting in the Church of Santa Francesca Romana, Rome. Oil on canvas. H. 18⅞″, W. 12¼″.
Gift of Dr. and Mrs. Walter Heil. 51.38.

Subleyras was taught to paint by his father. At the age of fifteen he started to work with Antoine Rivalz in Toulouse. In 1724 he went to Paris, where three years later he won the Grand Prize at the Academy Salon. Shortly afterwards he went to Rome and remained there for the rest of his life. Sponsored by important churchmen, he obtained numerous commissions for portraits and church decorations. This picture, like much of his work, is painted chiefly in shades of white and gray with only touches of color.

ALESSANDRO MAGNASCO.
Italian, Genoese, 1677-1749.
Soldiers Feasting.

Oil on canvas.
H. 23¼″, W. 17⅝″.
Purchased by the City and County of San Francisco.
49.7.

Magnasco's work was popular in his lifetime, but he was forgotten during the late eighteenth and nineteenth centuries. He was rediscovered early in this century, when his anticipation of the expressionistic trends in modern painting was recognized. His free and sketchy technique, pale, moon-like light, cluttered interiors that often seem like cellars, and thin, nervous figures lend a ghostly effect that makes his paintings fascinating.

GASPARO TRAVERSI.
Italian, Neapolitan, about 1725-1769.
The Fortune Teller *and* Merry Company.

Oil on canvas.
H. 26¾", W. 37¼"; H. 27", W. 37⅛".
Gift of Collis P. Huntington. 8549; 8550.

These Neapolitan pictures illustrate the survival
into the eighteenth century of the half-length genre
subjects which originated in Rome in the last decade
of the sixteenth century. They are all, in a sense,
the descendants of Caravaggio's celebrated
Fortune Teller in the Louvre, which in turn derives
from earlier Flemish paintings by such artists as
Massys. While the narrative element is not unduly
stressed in the two works by Traversi, Bonito's
painting would seem to represent a moralizing tale,
perhaps taken from a local proverb.

ATTRIBUTED TO
GIUSEPPE BONITO.
Italian, Neapolitan, 1707-1789.
The Diligent Daughter and the
Ne'er-do-well Son.

Oil on canvas.
H. 30½″, W. 41¼″.
Gift of the M. H. de Young Endowment Fund.
42.10.

UBALDO GANDOLFI.
Italian, Bolognese, 1728–1781.

Group Portrait.

Oil on canvas.
H. 46½″, W. 69⅛″.
Gift of the Samuel H. Kress Foundation.
61–44–20.

Ubaldo and his younger brother, Gaetano, were the leading painters of Bologna in the second half of the eighteenth century. The sitters for this remarkable group portrait are unknown, but it is assumed that the young artist is a self-portrait. It is likely that the elderly couple at the left and right are his parents, and that the nobleman whose portrait Ubaldo is painting is Count Ranuzzi, a patron of the artist and employer of his father. Notice that all the sitters except the Count look at the beholder, while the most piercing stare of all comes from the portrait.

MICHELE MARIESCHI.
Italian, Venetian, 1696-1743.
SS. Giovanni e Paolo and the Scuola di
S. Marco, Venice.

Oil on canvas.
H. 51", W. 66".
Purchased by the City and County of San Francisco.
48.1.

Marieschi, influenced by his contemporary Canaletto, was a painter of *vedute*, or views, of his native Venice. This school of painting was evidently inspired by Dutch cityscape painters visiting or working in Italy. Venice was a leading attraction for travelers from the north in this period, and these scenes were highly prized mementos of a southern journey. They were frequently designed with the aid of a *camera obscura*, a device known as early as the fifteenth century which, with a mirror and lens, projects an image onto a sheet of paper, allowing the artist to transfer the true perspective directly from nature.

ITALIAN, VENETIAN, LATE 17TH–EARLY 18TH CENTURY
Negro Slave.

Black marble and painted wood. H. 76″.
Gift of the California Midwinter Fair Commission.
3888.

The head, torso, and upper part of the drapery are of black marble; the lower drapery is of wood, painted to imitate stone. The theme of the statue is taken from the slave figures at the base of the statue of Grand Duke Ferdinand I of Tuscany in the Piazza della Darsena, Leghorn, by Pietro Tacca.

JOHANN JOACHIM KAENDLER.
German, 1706-1775.
Masonic Group.

Meissen. About 1745. Porcelain.
H. 9".
The Roscoe and Margaret Oakes Foundation.
L 61.4.11.

Subjects for these charming porcelain groups were drawn from many areas of life in the eighteenth century—drama, festivals, the trades, and many facets of life at court. In this group we see two Masons with their symbolic aprons examining a globe of the world. The angular disposition of the figures and the fluid movement of the glazed surfaces of the clothing help convey an impression of the lively interest of the two Masons in the subject they are discussing.

JOHANN JOACHIM KAENDLER.
German, 1706-1775.
Harlequin with Pug Dog.

Meissen. About 1745. Porcelain.
H. 6¾″.
The Roscoe and Margaret Oakes Foundation.
L 61.4.8.

For centuries it had been the dream of Europeans to manufacture "hard paste" porcelain as it was known in the much-treasured porcelains imported from China. It was not until 1708 that the alchemist Johann Friedrich Böttger discovered the secret of porcelain manufacture and found near Dresden a source of kaolin, the key ingredient for its manufacture. Two years later Augustus the Strong, Elector of Saxony, founded the first European porcelain factory at Meissen which maintained artistic leadership in the manufacture and decoration of porcelain for several decades. Kaendler, the modeler of this figure and many others in the Oakes collection, was director of the Meissen factory for many years and is considered to be one of the greatest porcelain sculptors of the eighteenth century.

JOHANN JOACHIM KAENDLER.
German, 1706-1775.
Crinoline Group.

Meissen. About 1740. Porcelain.
H. 7⅛″.
Gift of Hans Arnhold. 60.31.

Kaendler understood perhaps better than any
of his contemporaries the individual nature of
porcelain as a sculptural medium. It has a plastic
and light-reflecting quality possessed by no other
material. Kaendler exploited these characteristics to
the full in these small figures. Their subjects were
often taken from the popular comedies produced by
the Commedia dell'Arte. The figures in this group
represent Columbine and Beltrame.

FRANZ ANTON BUSTELLI.

Swiss, 1723-1763, active in Germany.

Lucinda and Ottavio.

Nymphenburg. About 1760. Porcelain.
H. 7¾″ (Lucinda), H. 7¼″ (Ottavio)
The Roscoe and Margaret Oakes Foundation.
L 61.4.3, 4.

This Swiss-Italian sculptor who worked at the Nymphenburg porcelain factory, one of Meissen's chief rivals, is generally considered to be the greatest of all modelers in porcelain. He is remarkable for his skill in contrasting plain and agitated surfaces and for his ability to convey by this means the spirit of his subject. These figures are from a set of sixteen characters from the Commedia dell'Arte plays modelled by Bustelli.

SIR HENRY RAEBURN.
Scottish, 1756-1823.

Sir Duncan Campbell, Bart.

About 1815. Oil on canvas.
H. 50⅜″, W. 40″.
The Roscoe and Margaret Oakes Foundation.
L 62.36.

Raeburn spent his entire career in his native
Edinburgh, where he painted most of the outstanding
men who were the foundation of that city's golden
age in the late eighteenth and early nineteenth
centuries. As this portrait admirably shows, Raeburn's
approach was entirely painterly; contemporary
accounts mention that his portraits were begun with
the brush without any preliminary drawing on
the canvas. The major's uniform provides Raeburn
with a rare opportunity to display his gifts
as a colorist.

JEAN BAPTISTE PATER.
French, 1695-1736.
Conversation Galante.

Oil on canvas.
H. 25⅞″, W. 32⅛″.
Gift of Brooke Postley. 59.36.

Another scene of aristocratic dalliance, in the same
vein as Lancret's set of decorative paintings.
Pater worked in Watteau's studio, and, like Lancet,
followed his style throughout his career. Pater's
scenes are generally more literally represented than
Watteau's dream-like, ethereal paintings.

NICOLAS LANCRET.

French, 1690-1743.

Breakfast Before the Hunt *and* The Bathers.

Two of a set of over-door decorations. Oil on canvas.
H. 23⅞″, W. 53″; H. 23⅞″, W. 51″.
Gift of Mrs. William Hayward. 53.2.2.

This series of decorative paintings fits into the specific category of painting (as defined by the Royal Academy of Painting and Sculpture, the final arbiter of taste in French art) known as *fêtes galantes*, or aristocratic pastimes and entertainment. A junior contemporary of Watteau, Lancret worked in the latter's style all his life. He gave his figures a greater sense of solidity than did most of Watteau's followers.

FRANÇOIS BOUCHER.
French, 1703-1770.

Diana and Callisto *and* Bacchantes.

Part of a set of paintings for Madame de Pompadour's
chateau at Bellevue. Signed: F. Boucher 1745";
"f Boucher." Oil on canvas.
H. 45¾", W. 36"; H. 46¼", W. 38".
The Roscoe and Margaret Oakes Foundation.
L 54.2; L 54.1.

The high water mark of taste which the vogue of
Madame de Pompadour signified during the
reign of Louis XV found in the art of François
Boucher its most complete expression in the art
of painting. His output was enormous;
hundreds of paintings and thousands of drawings
by him have survived. In addition, he produced
stage scenery and painted cartoons for tapestries at
the Gobelins and Beauvais factories of which
he became director in 1755. His graceful and
seductive figures are as charming today as when
they were the delight of the eighteenth
century connoisseur.

FRANÇOIS BOUCHER.
French, 1703-1770.
Mother and Child.

Signed: "Boucher." Oil on canvas.
H. 16¾", W. 13⅞".
Gift of Brooke Postley. 57.2.

Boucher, almost invariably associated with worldly
and pagan subjects, proves equally adept in
this simple domestic scene.

ATTRIBUTED TO FRANÇOIS BOUCHER.
French, 1703-1770.
Sketch for a Tapestry.

Oil on canvas.
H. 21¼", W. 43¼".
Gift of Dr. and Mrs. Rudolf J. Heinemann. 54.4.

When this handsome picture came to the museum it bore the title *Paris Abducting Helen of Troy* but it would seem, in the face of the air of public festivity on the quay and the presence of an Egyptian sphinx, rather to represent some episode in the history of Anthony and Cleopatra. This is the typical format for a tapestry sketch of the period dominated by Boucher. It also resembles studies by François de Troy.

JEAN MARC NATTIER.

French, 1685-1766.

Madame Boudrey as the Muse Erato.

Signed: "Nattier Pinxit 1752." Oil on canvas.
H. 51¼", W. 38⅛".
Gift of Roscoe and Margaret Oakes. 50.35.1.

Nattier enjoyed a thriving practice as a portrait painter, most of his sitters being from the court of Louis XV. His work was prized for its tender characterization, soft paint handling, and muted colors. He revived and popularized the allegorical portrait, in which the sitter is portrayed in the guise of a classical or legendary character.

JEAN-LOUIS LEMOYNE.
French, 1665-1755.
Pomona.

About 1720. Limestone.
H. 85".
Acquired through exchange. 60.12.

Lemoyne was one of a family of important painters, sculptors, and ornamentalists. He studied under Charles Antoine Coysevox, from whose hand the museum possesses a terracotta self-portrait. This early eighteenth-century sculpture of the goddess of the fruits of autumn was a garden piece which was once situated in the park of the chateau of Marly-le-Roi near Paris.

GERMAN, AACHEN, ABOUT 1740.
Paneled Room.

Oak.
L. 22′10½″, W. 16′5″, H. 11′6″.
Purchased with funds from various donors. 43.10.1.

This room comes from an eighteenth-century house designed by Joseph Couven for Johann von Wespian, mayor of Aachen (1734-1742). Carved in natural oak, the room is transitional in style, showing characteristics of both the Regence and Rococo styles in France, which at that time was the arbiter of taste for Europe. Most of the delicate low relief-carving still observes the symmetry of the early years of the century, but here and there, particularly in the over-mantel, one finds a bolder relief in the carving and the introduction of asymmetry in design. The tapestries, which are framed into the wall paneling, show how tapestries were meant to be an integral part of the interior. The ceiling is a reproduction based on photographs of the original room before it was moved. The paneling, which was slightly reduced in height, has been re-arranged into its present setting and represents about two-thirds of the original room, which was dispersed in 1901.

JACQUES VAN DER BORGHT.
Flemish, Brussels, active early 18th century.

The Poultry Market.

Tapestry, silk and wool. Signed: "I. VD Borght."
Brussels mark: " B B".
H. 9′3″, W. 8′.
Gift of the M. H. de Young Endowment Fund.

This is one of a set of four tapestries installed in the Wespian Room. The set was woven in the atelier of J. van der Borght probably after cartoons by the popular Dutch painter David Teniers the Younger. The subjects of the other three tapestries are: "Vegetable Market," "Milking," and "Vintage."

FRENCH, ROUEN, ABOUT 1740.
Paneled Room.

Oak heightened with gilding.
L. 28'7¼", W. 25'31½", H. to cornice 12'9⅜".
Gift of Roscoe and Margaret Oakes. 52.2.1.

This paneled room in the Rococo style of Louis XV
illustrates a unity of design which embraces the
fixed as well as the moveable elements in the
room. The curves to be seen in the carving of the
panels are repeated in the chairs, the table, the
commode, the clock, the andirons and girandoles, and
even the candlesticks. The trophies of musical
instruments in the upper panels probably
indicate that this chamber was originally intended
to be a music room. The curtain arrangement
is based upon the curtains represented in a
contemporary print entitled "Le Concert" by A. J.
Duclos after St. Auban.

FRENCH, ABOUT 1740.
Console Table.

Carved and gilded oak, Sarrancolin marble top.
L. 51", H. 33½", D. 21".
Gift of Roscoe and Margaret Oakes.
55.41.10.

This richly carved pier table shows the fully developed Rococo style with its curvilinear, asymmetrical design of scrolls, shell-like forms, Oriental dragons, and naturalistic swags of flowers. The table conveys a sense of richness and a feeling of unpredictable, ever-changing movement which admirably express the spirit of the period of Louis XV. Such pieces of immovable furniture were designed for a particular place in a room, and were often placed beneath a mirror whose frame was designed to echo the ornamental motifs of the table and the whole decoration of the interior of the room.

189

JEAN AVISSE.
French, Parisian, Master 1745.
Armchair.

Stamped on frame: "I AVISSE." Carved and gilded
beech frames, silk and wool tapestry upholstery.
H. 41", W. 26", D. 23".
Gift of Roscoe and Margaret Oakes. 53.29.6.

An excellent example, from a suite of five pieces, in the Rococo style of Louis XV. Chairs of this style are characterized by low backs, cabriole legs, flowing curvilinear lines which unite all parts of the frame, and delicate foliate carving. While tapestry is not the typical upholstery material of the period, it was occasionally used and, indeed, was a specialty of the Beauvais ateliers. François Boucher drew the cartoons for the tapestries on the chair backs representing personifications of the arts, and J. B. Oudry designed those on the chair seats referring to the fables of La Fontaine.

JEAN DESFORGES.
French, Parisian, Master 1739.
Commode.

About 1750. Frame stamped: "DF JME." Lacquered
wood, ormolu, and black Porto marble top.
L. 53", H. 34⅜", D. 23¼".
Gift of Roscoe and Margaret Oakes. 53.29.1.

The use of lacquer in European furniture was one of
many manifestations of an intense interest in
seventeenth and eighteenth century Europe
in the arts and manner of the peoples of
the Far East. This interest was stimulated by the
published accounts of travelers to the East beginning
with Marco Polo and by contacts established
by trade.

The marker's mark (DF) is stamped in the frame
below the marble top. The JME stamp indicates that
this piece of furniture had passed the required
inspection by the body of cabinetmakers appointed to
inspect the output of certain classes of furniture
to see that certain standards of quality
were maintained.

JEAN HONORÉ FRAGONARD.
French, 1732-1806.

The Good Mother.

After The Holy Family *by Rembrandt van Rijn in
the Hermitage, Leningrad. About 1773.*
Oil on canvas.
H. 18½", W. 22¼".
Gift of Mrs. Herbert Fleishhacker. 54.2.

Fragonard, one of the leading French Rococo artists,
is usually associated with delicate, intimate, gay
paintings; but he was highly impressed by the works
of Rembrandt. This charming study is one of a
series of details after Rembrandt's *Holy Family* which
was in the Crozat collection in Paris until 1772,
when it was purchased by Catherine the Great of
Russia.

JEAN BAPTISTE HUET.
French, 1745-1811.

Fox in a Chicken Yard.

Signed: "J. B. Huet 1776." Oil on canvas.
H. 38½″, W. 51½″.
Gift of Mrs. Frank Wilkins in Memory of
Charles LeGay. 50558.

Huet was admitted to the Academy in 1768, where he was a constant exhibitor until 1802. This painting was included in the Salon of 1769. His landscapes and animal studies were extremely popular; many of them were reproduced in large quantities in etchings and acquatints. In 1790 he was appointed to make designs for the Gobelins and Beauvais tapestry works.

JOSEPH SIFFRED DUPLESSIS.
French, 1725-1802.
Portrait of a Lady.

About 1785. Oil on canvas.
H. 24¼″, W. 19¾″.
Gift of the Family of M. H. de Young. 41.1.3.

Duplessis was a prolific portraitist of the nobility and royalty. He is noted for his free, broad technique and exceptionally harmonious coloring. It has been suggested, since Duplessis painted a pair of portraits of the Minister of Finance Jacques Necker and his wife, that this sitter is their daughter Madame de Staël, a prominent novelist active in society and politics during the Revolution and the Napoleonic era.

JEAN BAPTISTE GREUZE.
French, 1725-1805.

The Painter Étienne Jeaurat.

Oil on canvas.
H. 36¼″, W. 28¾″.
The Roscoe and Margaret Oakes Foundation.
L 53.44.

By 1741 the Salon, a semi-annual exhibition held by the Academy in the Louvre, had become an event of great popularity. It attracted large numbers of a public which, although ill-educated about art, was nevertheless highly enthusiastic. Artists began to cater to the taste of the crowds and were delighted when they won their approval. By mid-century the public favored anecdotal and moralizing pictures representing the activities and the solid virtues of the middle class; Greuze became a leading practitioner of this type of painting. He did some excellent portraits, such as this one, which also conformed to this mode.

CLAUDE MICHEL
(CALLED CLODION).
French, 1738-1814.
Nymph and Satyr.

Signed and dated: "Clodion 1778." Terra cotta.
H. 14".
Gift of the Roscoe and Margaret Oakes Foundation.
57.17.1.

Clodion, a pupil of his uncle Sigisbert Adam and later of Pigalle, became one of the most popular sculptors of the Louis XVI period. He was particularly noted for his *subjets libres* which were openly sensuous in nature. His small terracotta groups are especially sought after as Clodion excelled when working in a small scale.

ATTRIBUTED TO DAVID ROENTGEN.
French, Parisian, 1743-1807.
Secretary.

About 1775. Satinwood veneer and
marquetry, ormolu mounts.
L. 42″, H. 45″, D. 25″.
Gift of Roscoe and Margaret Oakes. 55.41.12.

Roentgen was one of the most celebrated of the many German-born cabinetmakers who worked for the French court. He particularly excelled in the execution of floral designs in marquetry (inlay of variously colored woods) and was famous for his skill in the design of mechanically activated devices connected with secret drawers and compartments. This desk displays his skill in both areas. It is transitional in style, artfully uniting the curvilinear design of the lower part of the desk with the rectangular framing of the roll-top front and the classically inspired gallery above.

FRANÇOIS II FOLIOT.
French, Parisian, Master 1773.
Settee (Canapé a la Turc).

About 1779. Beech; carved, painted, and gilded.
L. 90½″, H. 39½″, D. 31¼″.
Gift of the Roscoe and Margaret Oakes Foundation.
57.23.5.

While the settee is unstamped, surviving documents
suggest that it was probably part of a suite of
furniture commissioned by Marie-Antoinette for the
Grand Cabinet-interieur at Versailles and made
by Foliot in 1779 after designs by Jacques Gondoin
The settee was made for a particular alcove in
the apartment, but due to interior architectural
changes, the settee had to be shortened to fit its new
location. The documentary evidence of these
changes in the dimensions of the alcove and the
settee is a strong indication that the settee
was originally made for the palace.

ENGLISH, ABOUT 1770.
Settee.

Mahogany.
L. 53″, H. 38″, D. 19½″.
Gift of Frank Schwabacher. 56.38.5.

This piece from a suite consisting of a settee and four chairs is characteristically Chippendale in style with its pierced splats of richly carved mahogany.

Mahogany was the typical wood for fine furniture during most of the eighteenth century in England and the American colonies. The settee is conceived as an extended armchair with three splats and five legs. The carved ornament embodies a fusion of Chinese and European motifs.

While few pieces of furniture can be securely attributed to Thomas Chippendale's workshop, he had an enormous influence on furniture design in England and her colonies through the designs published in his *Gentleman and Cabinet-makers' Director*, the first edition of which appeared in 1754.

GERMAN, MEISSEN, 1737–41.
Platter from the "Swan" service.

Poreclain.
Diam. 13¾".
Gift of the Golden Gate Collectors on the occasion of their 25th anniversary.
65.21.

The platter, modeled by J. J. Kaendler, bears the arms of Count Heinrich Brühl (1700–1763) who was Administrator of the Meissen factory for thirty years. The decorative theme of the service was "water" and the flora, fauna and the mythology associated with it. The coming of the sculptor Kaendler to Meissen in 1731 gave great impetus to the use of relief and sculptural ornament in European porcelain. The Oriental influence, which had dominated the first two decades of porcelain manufacture at Meissen, survives in the scattered "Oriental" flowers to be seen in the border of the platter.

GERMAN, MEISSEN, ABOUT 1761.
Platter and Covered Dish.

Porcelain.
L. 15″, Diam. 11″.
Gift of The de Young Museum Society. 64.45.3, 1.

The dinner service from which these pieces came is said to have been made to the order of Frederick the Great, King of Prussia, as a gift to General Mollendorf, who served in the Seven Years' War. The reliefs of musical and astronomical instruments and flowers were presumably devised by Frederick in consultation with the Meissen artist Jacob Christian Klipfel.

FRENCH, PARIS, DATED 1776.
Paneled Room from the Hôtel St. James,
Place Vendôme, Paris.

Painted and gilded wood.
H. 14'6", W. 18'3", L. 25'1".
Gift of Roscoe and Margaret Oakes. 51.2.3.

This Louis XVI room provides a striking contrast in style to the adjacent music room of the Louis XV period. While a similar unity of style pervades the room and its furnishing, the style itself is entirely different. Here the straight line and the rectangle dominate the interior. The restlessness of the Rococo is replaced by a classic serenity. This renewed classicism is to be seen in the lines and proportions of the room and also in the many classical ornamental motifs which appear in the carved and gilded ornaments, and in the design of the chandelier, the furniture, the clock, the andirons, and the girandoles.

FRENCH, ÎLE DE FRANCE, ABOUT 1775.

Paneled Room.

Painted wood.
L. 23'11", W. 19'7", H. 11'5".
Gift of Mrs. E. John Magnin. 46.20.

This French room of the period of Louis XVI shows the influence of the classical revival of the second half of the eighteenth century. Of particular interest in this room are the decorations of urns and swags above the panels and mirrors, and the over-door reliefs of cherubs in the manner of the popular French sculptor Clodion.

JEAN-BAPTISTE BOULARD.
French, Parisian, Master 1754.

Chair.
One of a pair. Frame stamped: "I. B. Boulard".
Beech, carved and painted.
H. 35½", W. 19½", D. 18".
Gift of the Magowan Family Foundation. 64.18.1.

In 18th century France chairs were made by specialized craftsmen known as menuisiers. Their craft particularly concerned wood carving as is well illustrated in this pair of chairs in the Louis XVI style. Characteristic of this style is the use of straight lines in both construction and decoration and where curves are employed they are symmetrically used. Carved ornamentation is subdued and generally follows classical proportions and employs classical motifs.

DANIEL DE LOOSE.
French, Master 1767, died 1788.
Secretary.

*Mahogany veneer and marquetry, ormolu mounts,
About 1780.*
*Breche d'Aleps marble top. Signed: "D. de Loose."
L. 37¾", H. 57¼", D. 16½".*
Gift of Roscoe and Margaret Oakes. 54.10.

This secretary is in the fully developed classical style
of the period of Louis XVI. The curvilinear lines
of the preceding Rococo style have given way
to rectangular and asymmetrical forms in the desk's
shape and decoration. The ornamental
vocabulary abounds in classically inspired motifs such
as rosettes, triglyphs, and acanthus moldings.
This return to classicism in the second half of the
eighteenth century was in part inspired by
the archaeological discoveries made at Pompeii and
Herculaneum, the sites of which had been
discovered in 1738.

JEAN-ANTOINE HOUDON.
French, 1714-1828.
Madame Duquesnoy.

About 1800. Marble.
H. 26¾".
Gift of Roscoe and Margaret Oakes. 54.9.

Houdon was one of the greatest sculptors of his
period. He is particularly celebrated for his portrait
sculptures, three of which are to be found in the
de Young Museum. This bust, in addition to
its virtues as a portrait in the neoclassic style is
interesting for its portrayal of an elaborate coiffure
of about the year 1800. Rousseau, Franklin, Jefferson,
Lafayette, Molière, Napoleon, Voltaire, and
Washington are among the leading figures of his
time whose likenesses have been immortalized
by this French sculptor.

JEAN-ANTOINE HOUDON.
French, 1741-1828.

Voltaire.

Marble. Signed and dated: "HOUDON F. 1781."
H. 20".
Gift of Mrs. E. John Magnin. 61.31.

This is one of several versions of this subject executed by Houdon in marble, bronze, and terra cotta. While they differ in many details, such as dress, they are all based on a clay sketch made at a single sitting two days before the death of the celebrated French philosopher. This version is similar to one in the Victoria and Albert Museum, London, in which Voltaire is portrayed in Roman dress, a popular convention at the time.

THOMAS GAINSBOROUGH.

English, 1727-1788.

Samuel Kilderbee.

About 1755. Oil on canvas.
H. 50½", W. 40½".
Gift of the M. H. de Young Endowment Fund.
54479.

Before embarking on his career as a society portrait painter with his move to Bath in 1759, Gainsborough worked for nearly a decade in Ipswich. Samuel Kilderbee, a lifelong friend of Gainsborough, was a member of a prominent family there. Both the straightforward realism of the portrayal and the beautiful landscape, with its evening light, are typical of the portraits of his early period before he developed his later brilliant, virtuoso style.

SIR JOSHUA REYNOLDS.
English, 1723-1792.
The Marchioness of Townsend.

Oil on canvas.
H. 95″, W. 58″.
The Roscoe and Margaret Oakes Foundation.
L 62.37.

Through his painting and his activity as the first president of the Royal Academy, Reynolds did more than anyone else to make possible the flowering of the great school of English portraiture of the eighteenth and early nineteenth centuries. His inspiration here is clearly the full length format perfected by Van Dyck in his seventeenth-century portraits of the English aristocracy.

THOMAS GAINSBOROUGH.
English, 1727–1788.

Eleazer Davy, of the Grove, Yoxford, Suffolk.

About 1780. Oil on canvas.
H. 29″, W. 24″.
Gift of the Roscoe and Margaret Oakes Foundation.
66.2.

When Gainsborough moved to London in 1774 he established himself as a formidable rival to Sir Joshua Reynolds, who was recognized as the leading portrait painter of the realm. Though Reynolds was knighted and was head of the Royal Academy, the royal family preferred to be painted by Gainsborough. Not all of his clients were from the aristocracy; he did many portraits of prominent members of the merchant class, such as Davy. He insisted on painting his portraits in their entirety, refusing to make use of the commonly employed "drapery men."

SIR JOSHUA REYNOLDS.
English, 1723-1792.
Miss Boothby.

Painted 1758. Oil on canvas.
H. 30⅛", W. 25⅛".
Gift of Miss Carlotta Mabury. 55328.

Reynolds kept detailed records of his sitters and their appointments; it is known that this sitter, Miss Elizabeth Boothby, sat to him in 1758, early in the artist's career. His sitters came from many different strata of society, and his portraits show that Reynolds was as concerned with the character of the type to which the sitter belonged as with his individual character. His virtuosity led his contemporary and rival Gainsborough to utter his famous remark, "Damn him, how various he is."

THOMAS GAINSBOROUGH.
English, 1727-1788.
The Market Carts.

About 1778. Oil on canvas.
H. 50⅜″, W. 40⅜″.
The Roscoe and Margaret Oakes Foundation.
L 56.10.

During the years that Gainsborough spent in
Ipswich, his landscapes were usually painted
directly from nature and show the influence of
contemporary French and seventeenth-century
Dutch landscapes. In his later period, to which this
picture belongs, he developed a personal,
romantic style of landscape painting in which his
compositions were deliberate poetic inventions not
related to any specific scene. Gainsborough's clients
were not interested in landscapes, and he sold
very few of them. This picture belonged to his friend
Samuel Kilderbee of Ipswich, the sitter in
Gainsborough's portrait on page 208.

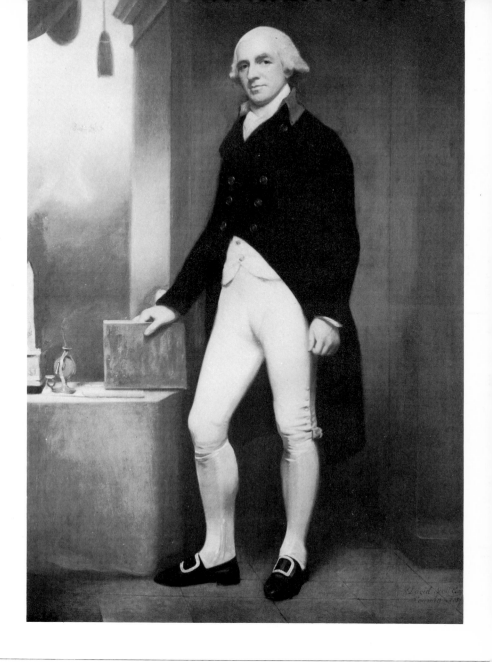

GEORGE ROMNEY.
English, 1734-1802.
David Scott.

Oil on canvas.
H. 92¾″, W. 60¼″.
Gift of the M. H. de Young Endowment Fund.
43.9.1.

Unlike Reynolds, Romney did not seek to project
the personality and character of the sitter onto canvas.
He specialized in likenesses generalized according
to the ideals of society, making him one of the
most successful fashionable portrait painters. His most
memorable sitter was the celebrated Lady Hamilton,
and he continued to reproduce her features long
after she had quit England for Naples. Bored with
the tedious business of portraiture, Romney always
yearned to paint historical canvases.

SIR HENRY RAEBURN.
Scottish, 1756-1823.
Sir William Napier, Bart.

Oil on canvas.
H. 59″, W. 58¾″.
Gift of the M. H. de Young Endowment Fund.
54650.

Edinburgh, known as the "Athens of the North," had its own school of portraiture rivaling that of London. Allan Ramsay, who worked at the same time as Reynolds and Gainsborough, actually held the title of Painter to King George III, though he seldom left Scotland. Raeburn, a contemporary of Lawrence, seems never to have had professional training but he developed in time a virtuoso handling of paint. The portrait of Napier is a fine example of the full length portrait which emphasizes the aristocratic breeding of the subject, but a far greater psychological penetration has been achieved in the delineation of the head of the commoner John Tait.

SIR HENRY RAEBURN.
Scottish, 1756-1823.
John Tait of Harvieston.

Oil on canvas.
H. 49⅛", W. 39".
Gift of Richard Gump. 59.50.

JACQUES LOUIS DAVID.

French, 1748-1825.

The Baroness Emilie Meunier, the Artist's Daughter.

Painted 1813. Oil on canvas.
H. 28¼″, W. 23⅝″.
The Roscoe and Margaret Oakes Foundation.
L 55.46.

It was the master of the Rococo, Boucher, who advised David to study with the Neoclassic painter Vien. The pupil soon outstripped the pallid accomplishments of his master and became the dominant figure of the era. The winning of the Prix de Rome, and his two long sojourns there, served to confirm and intensify his classical style, which was found to be perfectly suited to the moral and political aspirations of the time. In reaction to the despotism and frequent corruption of the *ancien régime,* David recalled the great examples of citizenship, the Greek and Roman republics. This painting, imbued with a controlled vitality characteristic of his portraits, is a product of his final period, during Napoleon's regime.

JOHN CONSTABLE.
English, 1776-1837.
Portrait of a Woman.

Oil on canvas.
H. 25¼″, W. 20⅞″.
Gift of The de Young Museum Society. 58.48.1.

Constable's fame as a great landscape painter has
eclipsed his accomplishment in portraiture. In
his early years he painted somewhat routine portraits
to increase his income, but late in his life, after his
reputation as a landscapist was established and
he no longer had to do portraiture for a living, he
painted a small number of portraits of outstanding
quality. This picture is marked by a freshness of
approach and the sparkling brilliancy of execution
that is found in Constable's work of this period.

AUGUSTIN ESTEVE.
Spanish, 1753-1809.
The Conde *and* Condessa de Castro Terreno.

Oil on canvas.
H. 78″, W. 45¼″; H. 78″, W. 45¼″.
Gift of Mr. and Mrs. Chauncey McCormick.
47.14.1, 2.

Esteve, a contemporary and follower of Goya, was a painter to the Spanish court; he is best known for his portraits of the nobility and of royalty.

FRANCISCO DE GOYA Y LUCIENTES.
Spanish, 1746-1828.

Don Ramón de Posada y Soto.

About 1801. Signed: "Goya." Oil on canvas.
H. 43⅜″, W. 33¾″.
Gift of the Samuel H. Kress Foundation. 61.44.26.

In his portraits Goya employed an uncompromising candor of vision, at times with unflattering results, as in his famous group portrait of the family of the corrupt King Charles IV in the Prada, Madrid. This portrait, however, records a more sympathetic personality; Don Ramón was a dedicated patron of the arts and a noted jurist. Goya's insistence on truth of characterization in portraiture is an integral part of his genius as a social and political critic.

CONSTANTIN MAKOVSKY.
Russian, 1839–1915.

The Russian Bride's Attire.
Signed: "K. Makovsky 1889".

Oil on canvas.
H. 10' 11", W. 13' 10".
Gift of M. H. de Young.
53161.

The Russian Bride's Attire, once the most popular painting in the museum, is still the largest. Though unique in this country, it is an excellent example of the 19th-century works which hang in the state museums of the Soviet Union, forming a visual record of the social customs of a Russia which no longer exists. Makovsky studied at the St. Petersburg Academy and was one of the student group who left in the historic 1863 protest against "academism." Before long he was himself an accepted Academician, Professor, and a mainstay of the official salons. Our picture came to the United States in 1904 as a part of the Russian exhibit at the St. Louis World's Fair.

LUIGI BAZZANI.
Italian, 1836–1927.

The Temple of Saturn.

Signed: "Luigi Bazzani ROMA 1894".
Oil on canvas. H. 44⅜", W. 23⅝".
Gift of M. H. de Young.
43239.

Though he was born in Bologna, Bazzani is chiefly remembered for a series of views which he painted of Roman monuments. They record, with the scrupulous detail of an historical document, the appearance of the Eternal City before it was overtaken by progress. In the rendering of the clear light that bathes the ruins, and the lively drawing of the small figures that inhabit them, Bazzani had no peers among Italian painters of the last half of the 19th century. One must turn back to the *veduta* painters of 18th-century Venice for suitable comparisons.

INDEX